KLEPTO

by
Nicky Allt

First edition published in November 2009 by Bang On Top
Publishing

ISBN 978-0-9564267-0-3

Typeset by Hope Services (Abingdon) Ltd

Printed and bound in Great Britain by CPI Cox & Wyman, Reading,
Berkshire.

Bang on Top Publishing
www.bangontop.com

It is the ambition of **Bang on Top Publishing** and this author to honestly depict an environment that existed thirty years ago in a certain strata of British life, rather than glorify the thief, hooligan or criminal.

While the **KLEPTO** story is essentially a true story, all characters, names and dates have been changed to protect innocent parties and those who paid a price, made good and gave up a life of crime.

Bang on Top

For Joseph Connor Allt, Georgia Bentley and Blaize Turner Coleman – The Brand New Generation – may you have the boundless energy, unswerving positive nature and passionate ambition of your parents!

Hoisters Handbook

Introduction

When I was first approached to write this story by first, Mickey Mac, then the Maloney's and eventually, the McArdle's, I knew in an instant it would ruffle some feathers. But, fact remains: Multitudes of young people from my generation, from the Northern part of Britain, ended up trapped in unemployment hotspots, the migrant worker lifestyle, or a dreaded, roller-coaster life of CRIME. So, feathers ruffled or not, this is a story about what happened to three of those kids.

Thatcher and her Tory henchmen sliced-up and steam-rollered hundreds of Northern communities. Then, thous-and's of those communities young person's hopes, dreams and aspirations. In the main, so THEY, not the majority population, could CAPITALISE!

Runaway CAPITALISM is not sustainable. There is a high price to be paid. Today, with World economic meltdown and people losing their jobs and houses on a grand scale, we are witnessing the backlash to high powered Political and Banking AVARICE!

Leaving school in the late seventies to mid-eighties, like those dreams, everything suddenly went SOUTH! Now, every single day, the son's and daughter's of MADAM PRUNE FEATURES insensitively trample all over each other in order just to keep up. Yet, we were told and sold on her lying doctrine that: GREED IS GOOD!

Well, speak for yourself oh GREEDY ONE! Yet, alas, I suppose you hardly ever get to review the results from a fortified MANSION in the posh suburbs! Still, you and your

1

SILVER SPOONED minions beware! There may just be a different world waiting around the corner from your own 'terrific' leafy suburb?

Note.
Although it's no excuse, fact remains that: while no job and no prospects will eventually equate to an unstable, poor, or *even* no family life for those concerned; for those with half-a-brain among them, the Devil will eventually find work for idle hands to do!

Show me a bright, ambitious kid with no prospects and I'll show you a potential thief and jailbird. Now, Put that in your Greed is Good pipe and smoke it!

Nicky Allt

Well I hope I don't die too soon
I pray the lord my soul to save
Oh I'll be a good boy, I'm trying so hard to behave
Because there's one thing I know, I'd like to live
Long enough to savour
That's when they finally put you in the ground
Ill stand on your grave and tramp the dirt down

To Thatcher: While you and your Government one day made the decision to trample on a whole generation, one day we'll decide to, TRAMP, THE DIRT, DOWN!

Elvis Costello

SET THE CONTROLS FOR THE HEART OF THE SUN

Visit to Miami Beach Florida July 2004

'May I help you Sir?' It's the question I've heard a million times. She gives me the old once-over – 'is he a spender?' I do likewise – 'is she a wise-arse?' Bit of a looker this one: mid forties, formally dressed with a rose scent from an English garden. She comes close enough to touch. Friendly type alright. Seems there's no body space conundrums' knocking about in that lacquered head of hers; totally polished with an all over Clinique sheen to things. I answer. 'No I'm okay, just looking thanks.'

She'd noticed me pawing over an expensive leather jacket – the dearest item on display – previous to me giving my mandatory reply. Miss Clinique, noting my tone, promptly affords me some decent body space but, more importantly, it should give *me* more time. Nodding an acknowledgement, she speaks as she moves away. 'And is that an English accent I detect?'

'Why yes. Is it so obvious?'

'Oh I love the English accent.'

'Why thank you.'

'Pleasure. If you need my assistance just holler for help.'

Overly taut skin tells regulation facelift stories; probably fifties then. She moves to the other side of the menswear department. Hopefully she'll waft her flowery breeze onto some other shoppers face and dutifully get on with serving them while I go about my business. An elderly gent looks for help. Could be green light for go. I'm fully in mode. Snips out, chain lifted, chain cut. Wait. Look. Miss Clinique leads the gentleman by the arm, leaning in attentively as though she might be hard of hearing or he might be mumbley of speech. Yeah, it's happening, it's looking good. No security cameras in view, it's all green light. Snips slip down the sleeve; chain lifted, squeeze hard...chain... eventually cut. Bit harder that time.

An additional scan of the menswear department tells me the ol' fella must have succumbed to her sales technique and seductive rose-like snort; either that, or the arms full of clothing they're both carrying says his wardrobe badly needs updating. Minor details, minor details! Get to it! From a fancy table display I place three Ralph Lauren Polo tops astride my arm; small, medium, large. Lifting the two paper-thin $1000 leathers by their hangers, I glide swiftly to the changing rooms.

Each time I enter the cubicles it reminds me of that silly *Stars in your eyes* show, only in reverse; the one with amiable but hairy, Mathew Kelly. You're in the shop, maybe you've got an audience; you act the shopper. Bit of snipping, clipping and viewing when you're sure the audience isn't having a gander, but outwardly, at all times, you do all you can to keep your happy shopping veneer well polished. Once you walk through that curtain you're a ravaging scoundrel, a bang on Hoister, a shady grafter on the make. Then it's just you! It's down to the real reason you're here...

Hangers lashed aside, ripping price tags from the sleeve, I quickly pull my baggy XL tee-shirt and lightweight jacket over my head in one. Cool lining meets a thin veil of sweat, as I put the first leatherjacket onto bare skin. It sticks. On the selling front, I'm hoping there's no sweat stains while I zip it up.

6

Dropping my elastic waist cargo shorts, I tie the other coat around my waist by the arms. Pulling the shorts back up, I tuck the jacket firmly down the sides till no bumps or creases remain. Difficult to bend as I reach for my tee-shirt, I lean far as possible to retrieve it from the changing room floor. Everything has stayed in its rightful place. Replacing shirt and jacket, I check appearance and breathing in the mirror. Picking up my fold-out mall guide, final checking my happy shopper veneer, I make my way out to civilization. Miss Clinique is still busy with the wrinkly. I'm off!

Before leaving the store entrance leading to the rest of the huge, Sawgrass Mills shopping mall, I scan the premises for roving Floorwalkers or would-be nosey Joe Public. A quick glance back to menswear shows Miss Clinique looking slightly puzzled. Shit! She's hovering over the jacket rack I've been snipping at. Lingering among the perfume aisles I watch her begin to panic. She's fumbling with the loose chain. It was a gamble returning to the jackets after she'd noticed me holding one up – that I know – and though it could be viewed through the eyes of a professional Hoister as a lazy mistake, it was a chance I couldn't pass. The two jackets alone were a days' wages in one swoop; sort of speculate to accumulate an' all that palaver. Never could resist a flutter in the sticky fingers game. Bastard! Eagle eye fucking cherry, she's spotted me. There's no question of putting the jackets back in place. Normally, anything shady and you simply get rid of evidence but, store chain massacred, with me carrying the cutters, means my on-board tool of use has just smothered that plan. Time to skedaddle!

Marching off into the mall walkway, I don't look back – not yet anyway. Ahead, I spot a uniform reaching for his radio. I can't turn back. Edging past, I hear him speak. 'Suspected theft in Dillard's department store, man seen leaving…'

Not hearing the rest as I walk by, I can't tell if he's onto me…keep walking.

7

Shoppers happily shop. Sales girl's chatter idly, nibbling sandwiches on walkway benches. Crumb cleaners push mops and brushes around the throng, while I play cat and mouse like a man possessed. Another mall security guy eyes me warily. His look stops me checking tail. They're onto me alright. No need to look back, I'm in Shit Street! They'll wait for a devious error in movement or till I reach my wheels, before tugging me. They're parked behind the store I've just copped from. Purposely, I've walked in the opposite direction. They're still not 100% about the perpetrator; who is in America? In the land of the counter-sue mentality they'll only tug me when evidence is overwhelming. I've got to shake tail.

Trying to act nonchalant, I move to an empty takeaway counter. Ordering a chocolate cookie and a drink lets me view proceedings best as. The uniforms are sitting-off in the distance. Bastard! – Miss Clinique is bang in tow. I'm more than the prime suspect now. Taking a huge gulp of Pepsi, I swallow ice cubes whole. Walking and baulking through the mall, I'm short circuiting with senses on overload. People walk by, oblivious to my plight. I suddenly envy them. The voice inside my head chooses its moment well, *I've told you a hundred times Mickey, you've got to stop lad*.

The first security mitt on my shoulder will be a jolting electric shock. The first voice aimed at me: a crashing cymbal and a banging end to freedom. *Don't walk too fast*. From the far corner of viewing range, I cast an eye over two more uniforms whispering into walkie-talkies. They're not like British shop police who try to camouflage up; nah, these gung-ho's wear stars and stripes and look you in the eye, as if to say, *'go on, fuck up, we're sure it's you, make a dash for it'*.

Mustn't panic, mustn't run. One simple approach and it's over; pray it doesn't come. I'm deciding whether to take the collar for what I have on me, or to try for a runner. Ahead of me lies JC Penney's, another large department store. Without thinking too much, I enter its bustle. I know my wheels are parked nearby as I've now walked the full length of the mall. Last-chance-saloon-voice tells me make a dash for the car and burn…that's unethical. Car chases and lifting simply don't go. It's making something trivial into something significant; especially to the bored shitless mall plod. If they search my vehicle – and they will – it won't be trivial when they find this morning's swag.

With the idea of buying something to stall for time, I head to the menswear department. A final glance behind lets me scan four security and Miss Clinique, all keeping distance. It feels like the whole mall is on the case. In the land of boom and consume, products are stacked high. The Berlin walls of shelved clothing afford me anonymity for a moment. I pick up a blue baseball cap. The drink, cookie and mall guide are lashed beneath the shelving. As Elvis once warbled, *it's now or never*. Pulling the jacket, tee- shirt and leather off in one, I shove the bundle under a heap of cheap jumpers lying astride a sales display. The leather peels away like skin. I'm soaked in sweat. Blink fast, a dark tee-shirt and Miami Dodger's cap are pulled onto body and head. Straighten up. Scanning a sales person making his way over, I dip into the next aisle.

Ripping a pair of red Hilfiger swimming shorts from a hanger, I kick my Rockport sandals under shelving before pulling them over my own heavier shorts mid-stride. It's time to walk the wall. You have to move along the inner perimeter of a department store to view proceedings best as; through the middle, its complete retail mish-mash.

The young sales guy pops his head around some shelving, like he's trying to find me. 'Excuse me sir, you finding every-thing alright?'

'Yeah, no problem; I'm just browsing while my wife bangs down the ol' plastic.'

'Oh, I see; the usual scenario.'

'You got it in one.'

Turning, he heads off to continue doing whatever he was

doing in the first place. It seems my heavy Mississippi drawl has been swallowed easy as off-the-bone meat from a baby back rib. On tiptoes, I look back towards the entrance for pursuers. I only see two guards with Miss Clinique. The others must be hunting in-store. It's definitely the Elvis now or never moment. Reaching the jewellery department gets me thinking about lifting some cheap shades. Nah...they always make people look more suspicious anyway. First guard looks me over. The bare feet seem to confuse then convince him I'm not the one. I don't dare linger my gaze too long. He passes by. Keeping an eye for the other guard, I walk the inner wall toward the exit door. Final glance back tells me there's a decent chance of escape. I just hope Sheriff John Brown isn't on exit duty. Now, I don't dare turn round. I'm gagging for daylight...

Shit! Passing under the A/C unit, through exit doors, the heat of the day and the Sheriff's cell on wheels hit me full in the face. Macho tash and shades; he's in the driving seat driving it, he's on door patrol. I see my wheels: a Ford Taurus. It's shouting me over. Above the JC Penney sign a black camera globe hovers like the mall's eye. Ignoring the calling of the Taurus, I keep walking. Scrambled calculation informs me an unseen store camera may well have tracked me from my initial clothes swap to exit. Fuck it! Blank the Taurus.

Another Sheriffs saloon comes swerving round the parked cars. He screeches to a stop, gesturing to the other patrol car. I'm seriously tempted to do a Michael Johnson across the hot tarmac of the car park. Again, toes twitching, it's tempting me. Once these bare feet touch black with speed, the race for freedom will be out of the blocks. I know that Books a Million bookstore is a good place to lose myself, but West Sunrise Boulevard is one long road to walk along out in the open, and though the mall is situated in Fort Lauderdale, like most US cities, the host city lies miles away from its main shop's. Thirty yards away a speeding Sheriff slams to a halt. Expecting the worse, I battle to remain passive. He shouts through the open window. 'You see a guy in a blue jacket, khaki's and sandals come by this exit just now?'

The Mississippi mumble is on auto. 'No Officer. An Officer inside asked the same thing. With that description, I'm on alert.'

'Thank you sir!'

He was off. Ahead, I see a drive-through bank; beyond, low-rise apartment blocks. That's where I'm headed. Forced to cross the open car park with the unhurried stroll of a local, I'm dying to run; especially with heels starting to melt. A hesitant peek over the shoulder shows three white patrol cars parked outside the JC Penney doorway. They're parked three or four spaces away from my freedom wheels. I couldn't risk them pulling me over if I'd gone for opening the door. One leather jacket and it's not too bad a charge; a boot full of Versace and Armani swag, tools of the trade and mall maps galore and its straight to the gang bangers mansion till bail is met.

Walking around overgrown shrubbery surrounding the bank reveals plenty of hiding specks for the brave. There's a swampy moat with wild undergrowth everywhere. Again, I check for bank cameras...none pointing this way. Either bush-tucker man bravery takes over and I dive, or I keep on plodding. In England I'd march on till a bus sauntered by to take me to new landscape, but this is Florida, and hardly anyone busses or traipses the street in doughnut country.

Diving into wild bushes Steve Irwin style, I'm receiving scratches and prickles galore; all the while ridiculously scanning for the odd gator or lizard. I'm familiar with local landscape. I've dragged a lawnmower over a few bumpy scales in my time; believe me, stranger things have happened than gators arse-parked outside a bank. Anywhere left overgrown in Florida rapidly becomes a sub-division to a number of wild, meat eating critters...sorry, animals...

Scattering gecko lizards and swamp rats rustle for cover as my weight snaps twigs. It's World War Shoplift as I find my speck in the trenches. I'm on the lookout for the security mall good guys; usually my bad guys. I can see the Ford Taurus and three Sheriff wagon's beyond. The exit doors of JC Penney's are surrounded by security guys nattering with cops. I'm definitely in with a shout for freedom. Wiping my brow, I need to clear vegetation hindering my spying patch. Got to get comfy; could be a long wait. Flashing lights and more troops show up. In England, it's you, the Floorwalker and Tommy Lone-Plod in a Wacky race. Any crime reported here, and it's you versus Uncle Sam, Corporal Clam and two hundred million Christian Crusaders. *Fucksake…I've got to stop!*

It doesn't get any easier this lifting lark. George Orwell wasn't far out with his *1984* Big brother theory; and things are only getting worse after 9/11. They'll be mounting cameras in toilets and changing rooms next, and all those dopey security goons will be fighting to get the best seat in the house for camera surveillance duty. Citizen protection technology apart, as you get older, you become aware you're picking up a few unconventional habits of the trade: looking over your shoulder for no reason; twitches here, suspicions there. Instead of clambering the ladder of society to gain yourself some healthy freedom, you find you've only fought your way into a barrel full of nervy spasms, with the constant need of an Atlantic Ocean cool-off becoming akin to the valium dependency of a depressed housewife. *Boy…do I know it's time to stop!*

Anyway, there you go; yesterday's close call. Three hours lying in that stinking Bank trench. Now it's Ocean cool-off time…well, as good as you can try to cool off here on Florida's Cocoa Beach. You could say I took the alternative route to wind up at this place. No charter seat with the happy Disney families for this leg of the journey. I'm lounging here at my little speck on Americas frying pan handle; a setting where the young at heart come to jump about, have fun and enjoy the rays, and the old at heart come to wind down, bide their time, reside, and yeah, enjoy some of those bone warming rays. Could be I'm lodged between the two. It's like the wrinklies have decided they want to feel as many tiny hot javelins of sunlight sinking into their cheekbones before the lights go out for good. They don't want to feel the chill anymore, only waves of warmth to keep those creaky old ribs permanently oven-ready.

Englishmen come here to call it a day, too. Me, I live here; but I'm far from wrinkly and finished. I did my 'Steve McQueen in a convertible', for the first few weeks, till the novelty wore off. Now it's blinding white tar melters almost all year round and top of the interstate temperature gauge nearly every day in July. TV weatherman keeps telling you nothing but, hot, hot, hot! Not nice, bone-warming hot, naughty, top of the cooker dial, tomato-nose hot. And how I got here? Well, for a start you'll usually find me down at this rickety old boardwalk, forever staring out over the Atlantic as the Disney cruise liners sail over the skyline; and, more often than not, I'll be thinking about how and why a cool breeze blew me to the Ocean gates of the planets biggest sunshine cemetery in the first place?

I mean, I've seen and grafted the world me, had a bit of a go an' all that; so why this joint? Beaches and sun, like a lot of the package crowd? Nah...never was a sun disciple: too much sweat, keeping still and sand up the crack of your arse for my liking. English mother tongue helps, I suppose – full-on westernized too. Could say there was quite a bit of the old Gulf-streamitis involved: chasing after that infinite warm wind... hmm...and the fact there's a Cockney wide-boy down the road who can sort you out a three grand, green card, might have had something to do with it. Yeah, that and the fact I can sail up the Gulf-stream all the way back home – Ha! In fact, make that double Ha! As if. Bit of psychological sailing you'd call that: comfort in knowing that loved ones and familiar streets lie directly across this vast Atlantic Ocean I'm always staring out at. But, let's face it; it's unlikely I'm going to take the trip. Love to though. No peace for the wicked eh! Uh, more like no snore for the poor on this pier. Thing is, those poor days are well behind me, and judging by the number of Board Rumbler's out in the sun, could be there's no chance of catching a snore with the on-pier skaters today.

See, I know I'm going-on about the heat, but boy have I got some serious sunshine; more than The Temptations ever wished for. More full-on stage lights in a month than my North West hometown seen in a year. Silvery white rays too, loads of it drilling into you're cheekbones. Enough to cure arthritis in a sixty year-old Bricklayers hands, or a forty year-old shop-lifter's being straight. Talking of being straight and stage lights, one of the roller skaters just darted straight into my stage-lights, and yeah, it's a definite lookalike. Here we go. Jerry Springer's skated right into the six yard area of my Atlantic Ocean penalty box. All it does now is silhouette his tatty head, bomb loud Hawaiian shirt, and white boater's shorts. Well, I say white, but if you include the Tony Roma, barbecue sauce stains, you're talking scruff-bag or shit-stained white. The cool breeze lifts his maypole fringe, scanning all loony tunes and flowing locks to me. His cheek-less backside goes back and forth. No peace for the wicked!

Round here, legs joined to the neck equals serial skater. Add this feller's look to a hung-on, porno, Magnum tash and you're watching Hannibal Lector's Florida fan club on wheels. Springer's wheeling towards what looks like a cased-up musical instrument? Maybe he's a bar mitzvah, wedding-type musician whose band never made the big time airwaves; sort of Springer ringer, wedding-singer…could be – God, I can't help myself, I've gone off on one again, thinking too much about some lunatics' minor details. He's started doing yoga on skates now…or something, and daft pirouettes? Hang on, I'm moving, I've got a story to tell here and Springer ringer's deffo damming up the flow.

Did I say damming up the flow? Is that Yankee patter? Scares me shitless I'm picking up the drawl – the lingo. Truly the first sign I'm turning into another cranky Yankee. And, I'll tell you something, this Cocoa Beach boardwalks not the one The Drifters sang about, nah, this ones the serial-killer conveyor belt, the choppem-up part of the Atlantic Ocean. Ok, a slight Hunter Thompson exaggeration, maybe, but they all look the part to me. It's like a transient supermarket this place, with lots of free offers: two for one's and stuff. Meantime, thoughts interrupted again, as Johnny fucken Space-cadet misses my sprawled out fingertips by the width of a psycho killers axe blade; and here's me thinking I'd finally found my own little space on the pier to reel off my Klepto tale.

'Keep your distance Spaceman!'

He's turned slightly.

'You heard me…YOU HEARD ME!'

Space-cadet's wearing the obligatory skater's headphones so he didn't really catch the jist about staying away. You'd think this astronaut would realize Cape Canaveral's further up the coast. You can even see the next space shuttle ready to shoot, parked-up like a rocket in a milk bottle. Too busy dreaming he's the Jon Bon Jovi of the beach this tit! Try it again motherfucker and you're going off the pier! Motherfucker! Motherfucker? It's lip-tripping time again; like I've been set helplessly adrift towards Americanization. Urban English caterpillar, to Stateside Yankee butterfly…sorry, motherfucking moth! An accent picked up in any State of the nation, redneck outcome, guaranteed!

I can't believe I've been here picking up the patter three and a half years now. It was all American gung-ho at first: new T-bone steak life, HBO Movies, stars and stripes bed linen the lot. I was mixed up then; grass is greener, land of opportunity an' all that. Easier shoplifting and having to run is nearer the truth. Now, three-grand down and green-carded-up, it's all homesick heartstrings, missing melancholy Sundays and that fine purveyor of warm bottled beer, the stinking English alehouse! Let me tell you, I never thought I'd say that. Though, has to be said, boozer was always a great place to sell any swag.

Hang on. This is getting beyond a joke. Another skater-come-lately has rumbled the board's right to the heart of my newly viewed Ocean scene. I'm going to give up on finding some drift-off the way this is going on. And yeah, no Major Ingram prizes for coughing-out-loud that it's another serial skater rollerblading on in. Here we go, my Nightmare on Cocoa Beach, as Freddie Kruger blades his way down the boards. Face like a baby croc this one; a portrait that could be sown onto every Lacoste shirt made in France. It doesn't look right that long, pointy face framed with a bouncy black wig; bit like the school bus driver in the Simpson's; bit ugly; bit aboriginal; bit like my old mate Boney, up close. And Boney, he'd love this place. 'Laid back to fuck' he'd say, almost permanently horizontal like him. Not a bit like Liverpool or London, nah, not like those English street-wise gaffs; at least here the sharks stay in the fucking water!

Being a people watcher – solely for grafting reasons – lets me know these predators on skates are looking for flesh alright; sniffing about for tenderloin. Half a brain, you can see them sidling-up a mile off. The crankiest busy themselves playing trap the transient or leech the loner. You see the low-life-fuckers on the local news every night of the week. Me, I'm a bit of a loner, but I've been around the people-watching-block a few times. Not like some naïve, young, fanciful Brittany looking for her own Jon Bon Jovi, happy to marry' n' carry her moons away from being just another hick from the sticks. Loads of them girls here, filling all those shitty vacation vacancies that only a runaway or someone hungry or hard-up will do. The British Job Centre could be sign posted Hotel jobs for Hicks along this coast.

All the while I'm grafting a living, the Jerry Springer's, Johnny Space Cadet's and Freddy Kruger's of the Space Coast are all sniffing around, waiting to play the big, bad wolf at Brittany's Motel door. And it's almost always screw-loose men on the prowl, isn't it. Except for that horse-faced, crank bitch from Florida, Aileen Wournoss, that is. Another Daytona World Champion; first at everything eh! Bet the Yanks are not so quick to claim that one. They've made a movie about her now: the female prostitute who bumped men off for loose change. 'Revenge of the pussy', the Florida dyke squad called it. What on earth attracted men to a pussy belonging to the winning filly at the end of a Grand National race goes beyond me? The Princess Anne of sunshine psycho's was a loose change predator, chipped-up about the men who'd teased her all her life and ready to blow. Here we go; lunatic details again, I'm supposed to be telling the Klepto tale…blame the dickhead skater!

The inner-city streets of Great Blighty were infested with money predators; no Wournoss, loose change merchants of note, more conmen, hand in your pocket, swindler types all after your fucking notes! At times you had to have eyes in the back of your head to stave off that crowd. My ol' mate Boney wouldn't have seen Wournoss coming, he didn't have eyes in the front of his head never mind the back; it's one of the reasons the kid never had a silver fucking sixpence!

I see a lot of young Florida kids who remind me of Boney down here. As you've probably noticed, it's all lookalikes and minor details in my Hoisting head: one of those compulsive dis-something's. I've tried stopping – it only gets worse. It's like hearing a record you hate on the car radio, in a shop, on the TV; next thing, you're humming the vile tune all day. It's like titchy, witchy, Kylie wriggling her tush and singing '*I just can't get you outa my head*' without the fillet mignon, bum-cheeks to save the song. And, it's all to do with the shoplifting game you know. See, lookalikes started out as a good way to let your memory register who was who inside all the different gaffs. Like you go, Tina Turner, she's the bird on the till every

Wednesday in that New Bond Street shop; or, oh its Ken Dodd walking the floor in Harrods today, simply because the girl on the till had gymnast legs and a head like a turkey on heat, and the store detective had crooked, sticky-out-teeth like the warped gravestones in an abandoned cemetery, and hair like the man who strapped a three-bar fire to his back before climbing into the bath!

Minor details kept you up to date with who was overly suspicious among shop staff, as in: who was getting bang on your case. It also kept you informed about new security measures a shop might undertake. Like, you'd go: 'the fella in the high roll-neck sweater – baldy-head – oh, Mr. Vibrator – yeah, eyes like cameras, be careful'; or, 'this shops started using a floorwalker and security tags, must've undertaken a stock-check and noticed the missing merchandise we've been taking the last few weeks'. All part of lifting lingo, I suppose some of it just stuck. Old habits die hard an' all that.

Boney was forever getting comparisons and lookalikes. They could range from Leo Sayer to Jimi Hendrix. He hated all of them. But he'd have been right at home with the laid back surfers and skaters. Lad never did care much for football or rugby, or overly aggressive weather, people, dogs, cats; fuck sake, you name it. Even those grumpy, old English pensioners always had a bee in their bonnet about something or other. You know the ones, *we won the war for the likes of you*, elbowing you in the ribs at bus-stops an' all that. Meantime, the rest of the World, over there, or, where I am now, are thinking we're all mellow mannered, English gentlemen – Ha! Another stereotype bites the British paving flags; in fact, double fucking Ha to that!

Thinking on, the happy holiday's tourist guide for Good 'ol Britain never did give a snifter to the seedy, smack-riddled side of Edinburgh, the down and out part of gangster riddled, landlord London, or the pint glass over the head side of casually cultured Liverpool. Oh no. Half of these dopey Yanks think we still live in some kind of semi-detached haven, round the corner from the Buckingham Palace gaff, all bowler hats and having a natter with ugly Prince Lugholes every time we pop round the corner shop to buy the Times.

Those film directors in Hollywood, they know the score, that's why all the movie baddies have an English accent. They might be able to tile half of Alaska with all the shit DVD's and videos they've made, but they're definitely onto the whereabouts of conman central. The rest of the cowboy population, I mean…forget it! Take yesterday at the pier for instance, some typical cranky Yankee on hearing my accent, after his gleaming teeth had asked me where I came from, starts enquiring if I lived near Paul McCartney and, if I knew him well – serious! Me, playing along with dim fucken Donny, I go, 'yeah, me and Macca go back a long way, he's been round for a barbecue a few times – rain-lashed sausages an' all that.'

Next thing, I'm signing autographs for the whole Osmond family, plus six or seven blood relatives, all jaw-stretched with the Donny and Marie smiles, all hovering for a little piece of the Beatles buddy. If they'd have took up the well advertised offer of cheap laser surgery in the Cocoa Beach area, before glancing at the signatures, they'd have realized I'd signed each one differently, with names ranging from Merrill the crazy horsed wanker, to, all the best, Little Jimmy McRing-sting, the long-haired lover from Liverpool.

Should be Florida State law to carry a Dazzle licence for those teeth; like the one they carry for the right to bear arms. Everybody knows they're more liberal with the guns and bullets over here: sort of everyman's right to be the Terminator. Laid-back on the outside, with a fucked-up terminators blood and guts on the inside; brains all frazzled like the meaty bits inside a beef and tomato pot noodle. Trust the Yanks eh! And get me – I'm talking about the American nation to a man here. Stereotyping? You bet! You've got pot noodle brain Bush, steroid-addled Arnie, and Ronny, un-fixed

Rubik-cube, Reagan, voted for in their millions by the air-guitarists of the USA. Need I say more? Want to find a crank – dial a fucking Yank! If there happens to be any reincarnation involved in this life, then I'd like to come back as Florida's first Uzi carrying roller skater terminator: the pot noodle commander bar-none.

I know I'm having a bit of a pop, but I don't belong at the gates of the sunshine cemetery. People come here to die. It's a massive burial site this Florida yard. You belong, or you don't belong. The reasons I don't: for a start, I'm an illegal alien from a rain swept, Northern British town and, as you've probably gathered, a shopkeeper's nightmare with knobs on. No British pride in that, but one false move, one stupid mistake, one unseen camera and I'll be knee-deep in God-botherers all the way to arse banditry and Clinkville!

And, it's not like Liberal Britain for the sticky fingered over here you know. No. You don't get five or six chances followed by a load of fines, community hours or trips to the Lake District. Nah, three half-decent Hoisting strikes and it's banged up in the Pen. I've pictured the route one way to get there a thousand times. It starts with John Wayne public, alias the store-detective apostles, wrestling me to the ground outside some high class department store; an' all in the name of Jesus Christ or the star spangled banner – depends which John Wayne tied his horse to the mall-doors while out shopping for some new Levi's. The picture always ends with me dossing-down in the sunshine slammer, while my supposedly foolproof green card gets scrutinized and pushed through the ministry mangle.

Oh yeah, you don't mention the other gods for now, not in America after the Twin Towers stuff. It's jam-packed with Christian God-botherers this place, like the crusades are still taking place, the satellite TV version: less obvious barbarism, more secretive brainwashing and more mighty religious dollars. Don't get me wrong, I'm no Atheist an' that, but I'm not on board with the righteous Republican on high brigade. Who knows with this crowd? Maybe they're all looking to be 'born again' because most of them are getting old? Wash away your sins an' that before it's too late? Yeah, looks to me like Florida's good ol' population could be suffering from a bad case of heaven just might exist.

After stuff disappearing inside coats, down pants and inside bags halfway around the world, I've eventually landed at this gaff. Yeah, I'm a Hoister; a one chromosome over the odds Klepto and, cutting to the chase, I'm on my toes. Not from the law, mind you, but from the poison powder gangsters who'd like me to take a tributary swim with some of those abandoned supermarket trolleys. So, stating the obvious, I'm not what you'd call a happy Hoister. And, before we go on any journey an' that, let's start out straight: the swag I blag, it's all just stuff. Stuff to buy you some freedom and a decent roof, and that's it!

Don't ask me up front for the Christian guilt card, I had that one shoved at me in abundance. As I've said, I'm no Atheist, but these days the guilt has mostly been dealt with. I've now got a small Landscape business up and running; part of my green card deal, and yeah, I lifted the lawnmowers...Well, not lifted: sort of drove them away from the Home Depot, DIY doorway, if you get my drift. I've got top of the range grass-manglers I have; no extended warranties though. Yeah, always a bit of a light fingered Larry that was me after leaving school – especially when the first few jobs round our way quickly left me. Always wanted to be a journo, or a Pilot, something that moved around – wasn't tied down. That kind of job wasn't anywhere near my flight path when I took off to the big world. As far as degrees, Uni and good-graft goes, not *a* bleeding snifter, but concerning drudgery, factories and pittance, well, surprise, surprise, absolutely bang-on the in-collar-agenda.

I don't know anybody here, you know, like me, light fingered an' all that, but I know there's others, I've seen them

21

lurking by the shelves. Listen to me, David fucken Vincent, on about the alien Shop Invaders. It happens though. They clock me, I clock them, we nod, we take, we go. Nodding and clocking apart, I'm scared that too long in the sunshine cemetery and a bad case of Pot noodle brain is bound to start seeping through; leading to a few dim-Donny moments; leading to me, clapped in irons. I've got to pack it in. Boney would've still loved it here though. That lad's brain was always Pot-noodle'd.

Anyway, enough Florida rattle, suppose what you'd really like to know is why light fingered Larry ended up on his toes telling you all this at the cemetery gates in the first place. See, I'm squirming a bit, as I don't wish to start out sounding like some kind of loopy lifter. Thing is, it only started out as a normal holiday at first. True, I had to leave a bit sharpish, but that was always par for the course with me. It began with, you know, usual dreary English summer, with me and the missus, like half the parents in the country, thinking about taking the two kids to a Sunny D place. Knock on the door one night, and I'm a wanted man. Florida's on offer, so Florida it is.

Driving out to Orlando's nearest beach one day, we stopped for a bite to eat at one of those Ten Dollar buffet joints. Food walloped, we parked the hire car at a beachside Hilton hotel. The sea looked gorgeous. That was it…I'm in. I copped a load of towels from the hotel pool area and, as the family settled on the sand I bombed straight into the surf. Enjoying a nice, leisurely dip and, seeing as the water felt warm, I quickly changed into Johnny Weissmuller mode to show the kids how far out I could swim. If I'm honest, it was showing-off to a certain extent. Suddenly, I started getting these killer cramps, the electric shock variety that renders you helpless, especially in deep water. No illnesses or weaknesses or anything, nah, just me paying the price for acting the Mark Spitz too early. I'd polished off way-too-much tucker at the $10 buffet, a local custom in Florida, a local custom now dragging me under…

Next thing, belly bloated, I'm swallowing half the Atlantic Ocean as a salty, after dinner drink and can't do fuck all about it. Struggling, meanwhile, only makes things worse, when those heavy cramps start to zap at your kidneys. It's like a mermaid Mike Tyson lying low underwater, waiting to sneak up and hit you with deadly uppercuts and body blows when you're at your most vulnerable. The undertow started dragging me back and I began to sink underneath. The strong current and the mermaid Mike Tyson were clearly winning the fight. With nobody out that far, no one could hear my silent scream. Drifting further under, my toes couldn't find the bottom. I'm thinking, *'I'm not ready yet. Don't let go. Why now?'*

A final ray of sunlight skimmed off my forehead through a chink in the Ocean surface, as the water zipped-up like a body bag all around me. I was out of sight. I was gone. It was that quick.

The water enveloped me as the panic unexpectedly subsided. My brain signaled for me to attempt a struggle. My body didn't respond. My brain said try again. It was pointless, my limbs were too heavy. I felt paralyzed. Once I relaxed, calmness washed over me and the fleetingly distant sunlight appeared underwater in the form of a neon staircase. Mad eh! It felt warm and comforting. I could see the dark shapes of people trying to pull me up, but felt unsure. They seemed strangely familiar, like relatives come to help me because I was lost. Their arms reached out reassuringly. Their actions told me it was nice where they were: warm and welcoming at the top of the staircase. Boy, believe me, I was tempted...

Then, I'm drifting; drifting peacefully in the liquid abyss. I'm looking up at them, the fight in me, long gone. It seemed glorious where they were. Who are they? I couldn't make them out, but in the bull's-eye of my heart, I knew I knew them. Thinking about going where they were, their hands reached out to pull me up. Immersed peacefully undersea, my mind's eye pictured my family without me. They were sat with an

23

explaining uniformed Policeman, looking utterly distraught; overwhelmingly upset...WHHOOAA! I was suddenly fighting back, clawing my way to the surface. A gap in the Ocean began to open up, before a turquoise sky eventually greeted my re-emergence into daylight. The cramps were gone, my arms and legs felt light again. I started doggy paddling like a learner. It was good enough to keep me afloat. I knew instantly what had happened. I'd known and seen this scenario before. Swimming baths – school – twelve years of age, the warm white staircase and comforting arms beckoning me to its pinnacle. I'd nearly died. It had occurred again. Why here?

That was three years ago now, and with a few baddies on my case and, for whatever other reason, I kept coming back to this Florida yard, like the place was spiritual or something. My own cross Atlantic pilgrimage – Ha! Getting all philosophical about near-death and seeing the white light again. Anyway, who knows? One thing I do know, it's finally peaceful down here, so its time I started telling you about my buddies... sorry... mates, and all the craziest parts of a Hoisters journey, and how this shoplifting thing kicked-off and kicked-in back in 'Forty Shades of Green' country.

With no more pain-in-the-arse Board Rumbler's about, it shouldn't be a problem. See, I'm clocking the back of the curly-haired, space cadet now, and as the Simpson's bus driver skates off down the pier surrounded by orange circular sunrays, it gives me Boney's silhouette once again, and with no more skate cadets about, its tranquil, its drift-off, it's easy, I'm back in mid-eighties London again, I'm up on my toes again, and yeah, as usual, it's down to the Bone again.

2

SHIRTLIFTER'S WITH A SAUCERFUL OF SECRETS

Zooming in good and tight, Boney's got that familiar blood-drained look on his gob: bit like the fat kid on the ghost train who's eaten too many of mummies fried eggs for breakfast. I'd seen that look before; instantly recognized as his bang on top face. Coming up the basement stairs in too much of a hurry for my liking, I clocked behind him…yep, sure enough the shop assistant plus the acne-scarred Floorwalker were both acting sly in slipstream. Looking in the direction of Tottenham Court Rd tube station my toes began to twitch. Full comprehension twanged me; it was the moment of skedaddle. Olympic race face – rev the engines boy.

Stepping away from the door, drawing attention away from myself, I quickly scanned the street. No Bizzies, no Snides and, I hoped, no wannabe heroes. The last thing I needed on today's agenda was a serious legger, due to the fact I was wearing 36"waist trousers, while I was really a slim-line 32". For obvious reasons you had to be more six-pack Linford Christie, than love-handle Barry White in this job. The extra inches meant you could carry the swag out of the shop without breaking stride and, I still hadn't had a fill yet. If I had to run full-pelt they'd only hinder progress, or end up in a heap around my knees as I performed the Coco, which meant giving it toes down the street while holding the waistband up.

Usually we'd just slot the gear in a large, sown-in, inside pocket or deep under the armpit, but getting greedy for extra income, the Barry White pants were back in town. Though we knew the heavyweight smooch-king was more 56" than 36", the name stuck. Extra income – wear Barry's pants. *Come on Boney lad, just ignore me.*

Unwritten lifters law stated: whoever came to the attention of shop-staff would give only the faintest of signals or the slightest of nods. Doing things this way, the person getting unwanted bleepers wouldn't have to reveal the identity of their partners in crime. Boney boy had broken this law before, but I hoped by now the penny had dropped and, the same penny had lodged somewhere inside his scattered, egg fu yung of a brain.

'Run Mickey run, its bang on top!'

Shouting directly into my face while I perform my office lunch-hour impression, ends all hope. Then he calls across the road to Paddy, our bagman. 'Give it toes Paddy!'

Paddy tries to blank him. He won't have any of it.

'Leggit! Its fucken bang on top!'

King of the 50 watt bulbs had broken simple lifters law again. Nobody had poured the boiling water over his brain to release the flavour; his juices were not in tandem with the Hoisting game and, due to ignorance regarding codes of practice, my office-bod impression had just sailed straight up the Suwannee. For a split second, last chance, I try ignoring the dried-up noodle-brain, but he grabs my arm, which in turn gives me a full part in the scenario. I'm out in the open. I'm fucked. Time to grab the waistband!

I knew I'd regret feeling sorry for soft-shite the moment I caved in after listening to his whining voice monotonously drowning out the football commentary the other day. Poor lad had cried down my ear for almost the whole of the second-half of the England versus Argentina, World Cup Quarter Final. You know the one: where the little fat Dago…err, sorry, Diego, punched the ball into the net. I hardly saw the game due to his constant fucking whining.

'Ah come on Mickey, how long have we been mates? You know I need the dough.'

'You made a good few bob the other week. Where's that gone?' I asked.

'I've sent it home to me Ma, so she can get to Benidorm with all the other oul ones.'

'Don't talk shite, dozy-hole; you wouldn't send your Ma a cellotape'd fiver if you'd just hit the paraffin lamps jackpot on Lester Piggot!'

Like a true Hollywood drama queen, he gives me the big Shirley Temple eyes and hits me with 'Come on Mickey, don't be like that; you know if the three of us stick together we can go a helluva long way.'

'Ha ha, yeah alright Boney lad; you mean all the way to Wormwood fucken Scrubs!'

'Ah don't be like that. You know when I'm famous on the telly I'll look after you and Paddy.'

Hilariously, he'd been taking acting lessons while we were all grafting down in London; adding the illiterate Gene Wilder to the night class numbers and to his own growing list of stupid lookalikes. My momentary silence only encouraged him.

'They always want somebody to play a Liverpool fella, you know, like Tony Booth in that Alf Garnett thing.'

'Till death us do part, you mean?'

'Yeah, yeah that's the one.'

I mean, as fucking if! We're talking about a lad who struggled to converse in his native Liverpudlian Scouse, never mind juggling with Thespian English, or oinky, twoinky regional twang. Boney taking acting lessons was akin to Jethro from the Beverley Hillbillies auditioning for Shakespeare's Twelfth Night. He's going on and on and on. I just want to see the last twenty minutes of the football. Finally, I relent. 'Alright, alright, just shut the fuck up will yer!'

But he didn't; he never did. Now the gormless Gene Wilder had us acting the part in his own London version of Stir Crazy, while our own court appearance began to look ominous as we gave it toes up Tottenham Court Rd on a sunny, Tuesday afternoon. Paddy and I were only missing Gene Wilder and Richard Pryor's two yellow chicken suits from the movie to make the scene believable. Sometimes I wondered why Boney didn't hang a neon sign on the back of his coat saying, Watchout! Our firms on the Hoist today!

Speeding past the umpteenth electrical retail store on the street, I started to think, *it's not gonna be long before somebody on the pavement catches our reflection in the shop window;* which was bound to switch their attention from the TV they might be intending to take a hire-purchase agreement out on, to the three sprinting scallywags intent on making a dash for freedom behind them. A high speed hero shows up on Main Street somewhere in the world, in every minute of every day and, you know what a shoplifter says about a would-be retail hero: got arms like air-tight, adjustable spanners in the headlock stakes, and normally proud, let's clean up the street, medal wearers to a man. Boney, Boney, Boney, always the dimmest light bulb in the DIY store. Paddy's going nuts, shouting, 'You again, only you could get us into this. That's your last Boney boy. You're back by yourself on the building site Monday!'

Running towards Oxford Street, only one shop worker kept chase. Deciding to jump down a small side street before Joe public got involved, we waited for Shop Guy behind a couple of those big, steel food bins; puffin, panting, panting, puffin. Soon as he entered the narrow walkway he was on to us. I stepped out. 'Listen mate, no need to be a hero.'

Relieved to see he was definitely shop-staff and not the acne-faced Floorwalker we'd spotted a mile-off, I relaxed a little. That other spotty, spare prick had sneaked about like a tidal wave inside the shop. Those tiptoeing, granny and granddad grabbers always gave the impression they were all wannabe coppers that failed the Plod exam, and were now getting used to seventh or eighth on the law enforcement job ladder. Failure in the exam emanating from a massive lack in undercover disguise technique; and this latest blotchy ornament, I must say, was the glitter-ball of all store detectives. Playing shop dummy impressionist or peek-a-boo through the shelves was never going to be his forte; the fella stood-out so much. We'd clocked him a few times before and there was no way you could miss that beans on toast face.

Eyeballing shop staff, I street greeted him. 'We don't want any violence just for the sake of a few shirts. So, if we hand them back to yer, is everything custy?'

Close-up, I clicked he was a dead ringer for the lead singer from The Pogues, even down to the twenty Mars Bars a day teeth. Staring at the three of us, he's saying nothing. I repeated, 'If we hand them back to you, is everything custy?'

This double wardrobe, rugby-playing-type, who looks like he'd come up trumps after a flying body-check on a London bus, has gone all lip-sealed, staring blankly in our direction. I'm thinking, *he's either getting ready to throw a big right-hander, or he's going to show us those piano-key peggies again by bursting into a rendition of 'Dirty Old Town'.*

Wrong on both accounts; in the snootiest English voice you've heard since Queen Lizzies speech on Christmas day, he spoke up. 'What does custy mean?'

Well, with all the tension and everything, it felt as though he'd stuck a pin into the balloon of back-alley confrontation. We all burst out laughing; including Shane McGowan himself. It was a good sign. Studying his face had me register him a non-screamer. I offered peace. 'Give the man his merchandise Boney.'

Boney, reaching into his tailor made pockets, pulled out three designer shirts and handed them over.

Before posh Shane departed we got a blimp of his Sugar

Puff peggies again as he enquired in that Sloane ranger accent of his. 'Now you won't be coming back to visit our little establishment will you fellers?'

Resisting the urge to tell him to get down to the dentist's for a new set of railings, I replied. 'No Sirree! Not in this lifetime!'

A final look into Shane's eyes told me he was ready to walk the happy walk of truce without having to change into a Police siren. Flashing me his piano key smile for the final time, I thought how that accent and those teeth didn't go together; leaving me to concur it had to be down to too many chocolate buttons getting downed as an energy boost during the half-time rugby interval. I mean, the fella was just too bulky to be a lunchtime smackhead. Glancing at the other two, I realized all of us were under starters, revving the engines to make haste. The moment I gave the signal we skedaddled as far from the confrontation station as possible, till the first person's stamina gave out. Eventually, Paddy, the only smoker, raised his hand and coughed. 'Eno...u,u,ugh,' before gruffly shouting, 'ENOUGH!'

I'd been anticipating his lung-master's call. As usual, he'd been coughing and spluttering over the last hundred yards or so like a Q reg. Volkswagen Beetle. Breathing comfortably, we proceeded to give Boney a severe toe-ending. Wincing in pain because there was never enough meat to protect his pink rosette from a well aimed brogue, we told him he'd had all the chances he was ever going to get; which translated as: till the next time he moaned non-stop for two hours while giving you his sad, Oliver Twist, 'can I have some more' face. We had to laugh though, handing the shirts back he'd said nothing about the other five sitting in the lining of his coat...Twenties all day on those gorgeous John Smedley sweaters.

Boney, being a rattler inside the shop, meant anyone with an inkling of suspicion could see him openly gawping at staff as he slotted gear; making it obvious what he was up to. It took him an age to focus on things with those bats eyes of his. Preferring him out on the pavement, we'd got him clutching the swagbag, which held the day's takings, while keeping Dixie on the street. Thinking about Boney watching over proceedings, I have to giggle. The lad struggled to read the Adidas sign on the side of the large, blue sports bag we carried around. I imagined his street scene appearing like a school kid's collage: a cluttered-up, mish-mash of people, with cars and buildings colliding into one. If old Officer Dibble did happen to mosey on by, the only thing you could be sure of was Boney being the last to know.

Being most of the way up Charing Cross Road, I knew if we carried on we'd end up at Covent Garden, an area well populated with designer labels and fancy-dan fashion accessories – all with cool London price tags to match.

Noticing a large Menswear shop called Take Six, I looked at Paddy, nodding in the direction of the shop with the sole intention of doing just that. Without a word he walked to the door. I gestured to Boney to walk on by. He stared at me baffled. I muttered through clenched teeth. 'Just wait down the road.'

'Why? What for?'

Halfway through the shop doorway I got to the point. 'Boney. Fuck-off! Now!'

Getting the message, he did an about turn up the street and, thankfully for us, directly away from the shop. Entering, Paddy already held up a black pair of formal pants. Making my way over, eyes scanning the shop floor, I took in the whole shop scene in one take. The message came back affirmative. It was time to get right to it. Paddy clocked me sidling up. 'Looks custy to me.'

I go, 'Okay, stay there, don't move.'

Rolling three pair of pants, I pushed them snugly into my large, inside pocket. I have to bend slightly undertaking this action: knees bend, arms stretch, la, la, la, la, la. Soon as I've

31

bowed and finished, as in two seconds later, I scanned the floor for a second time. Not too much, mind you; don't want anybody inside the premises to think I'm Shaking Stevens, Boney's nosey half-brother out for the day on lifting patrol.

'Looking alright to me boy; stay there Paddy while I get another fill.'

Slowly rolling three more pair till they form a tight bundle, I'm thinking, *well the shop sign did say Take Six*. Sticking to a set order keeps things neat and tidy; no set plan can end up grabby and messy. And, the thing is, you have to go slow. Try to roll them up too fast and they end up in a launderette bundle. A disorderly parcel usually equates to an earning moment lost. Untidy launderette bundles don't glide-in. Pants neatly bundled portion of chips style, one quick scan and Roberts your Aunty, snug as a bug in a sugary mug. Downside, you don't usually get time to check the size. No sooner have the pants reached destination, than I'm already hoping I haven't picked up any 44 inch waists from the rail. We were in lean and mean London, not fat twat Florida. In lean and mean country they were never fast sellers those Pavarotti pants. The loose pair you wore was all you required for a Barry White day.

'Paddy, move away from this speck; them shirts over there look tasty.'

A slight gap opened on the pants rail. It was in our interests to get away from the vicinity of the missing strides, soon as. Gaps on rails are like gaps in front teeth: they draw unwanted attention from beady eyes.

Reaching the shirt display, I afforded myself another survey of the shop floor. The picture coming back was of three staff members busy serving customers, while three or four other customers stood impatiently waiting to be served. Designer establishments always skimp on staff, but who am I to moan, it only works in our favour. It's unlikely I'll be carrying the flag for any striking, overworked shop slaves on this, or any other afternoon.

While scanning, my bleepers also have to log any nosey customers who might fancy turning Queen's evidence. Maybe they're thinking they might be in line for a little discount if they snitch on the shoplifters. Forget it! Law abiding Joe and Mary of the public, let me tell you, they never give you a penny back these clobber joints. They tell you it's your duty as a citizen and, that prices will only go up if you don't blow the whistle. Well, here's a big double Ha! to that. No matter what whistle you whistle into, or what profit they make this year and every year, nothing is going down in price with the fast buck, rag-trade-blaggers; not unless its stuff they're struggling to push through the till-drawer that is, like a few dozen pairs of Pavarotti pants.

Paddy's looking for guidance. 'What's it saying?'

'It's saying you're alright.'

'Like now?'

'Yeah, like now. Go on its sweet.'

I've got one eye sweeping the premises and one eye on Paddy's Barbour coated back; in other words: eyes shifty as fuck. First I see the bulge in the side of his coat from the shirts he's bundled up; then I hear the rustling noise as he forces them to drop. Eventually they nestle into the bottom of his inside pocket. I realize his binning action is over when he stands fully upright and straightens his coat. Wondering whether the coat bulge is too obvious, or whether shop-staff have taken undue notice, I let him know it's all looking rather neat. I'm getting green light: time to proceed; time to move to go.

'Everything's tidy brother; looks like the moment of skedaddle.'

Paddy, like a sailor checking for land on the horizon has a scan of his own and says, 'We straight out the door or what?'

'No, follow me over here first.'

Pretending to look at some suave shoes on the other side of the gaff affords us a final check. It also makes sure we leave the joint looking like a couple of everyday shoppers. Don't

33

need to give off the appearance to unknown prying eyes that basically we're a pair of happy Hoisters just bounced in off the pavement to cop for a load of gear. When I know we're safely out of earshot, nowhere near the racks we've taken items from, I tell Paddy, 'Looking alright to me; skedaddle, or what?'

'Yeah, come on, let's do one.'

First few steps onto the pavement – usually a final pointer to whether any staff are on your tail – means it's time for me and Paddy to partake in a game of *first man to clock Boney*. An infuriating pastime when you're concealing merchandise, and the only pointing to be done is by Paddy or myself as we point in all directions at things or people that might lead us to the Harpo Marx member of our firm. Like the kid who blew a hundred Fairy Liquid bubbles, my eyes took in the vibrant, Covent Garden street scene. Failing to catch a glimpse of Boney, either my eyes were getting bad as his or, he'd drifted out of sight again. Paddy's look betrayed his own confusion as realization set in that the search was going nowhere. All this after Boney had been told for the umpteenth time not to go missing when we were loaded up with swag. What a tool!

Walking in search of a curly, black bonce, the area teemed with the same type noggin. Eccentric Bohemian's, seated artists and street performers lay dotted all about the Covent Garden area. Paddy, fed-up phewing and tutting, called out. 'Over there. See that betting office; check that!'

Opening the gamblers favourite door, Boney's woolly-skull came into view. Surrounded by cigarette smoke, deep in horse racing gibberish along with some other woolly-headed, betting office merchant, we snuck over to gauge the lingo. Placing ourselves behind the two gambling perms, we heard Boney first. 'So every time yer get paid for doing a painting of someone in the street, yer go and put a bet on straight away?'

The other guy, a young Marc Bolan wearing a loud, court jester's outfit, answered. 'Yeah, assright, I just do ma pictures, then I cam and place ma bet.'

34

The voice, slightly effeminate, slow and Mick Jaggeresque, had me smiling. I wanted to remain deadly serious. Before they caught us ear-wigging Paddy stepped between the two. 'Can we interrupt this meeting of the Billy Smarts circus please?'

The clown looked puzzled as Boney jumped to an answer. 'Paddy, Mickey, meet me mate, his names Clementine.'

Paddy goes, 'Clementine!'

I battled to remain straight-faced. 'Shut the fuck up Boney, and get outside now!'

Clementine didn't bat an eyelid, and spoke to Boney in his slow, Southern English drawl. 'Awill see you before the next race, Aaannnthonnny.'

Making Boney's Christian name sound like a symphony, I spoke up. 'Oh Anthony is it? Well get the fuck outside Anthony; and right now if you don't mind.' Adding, 'Aaannnthony'll be gone for a while, Mr. Fucken sssllooww Taaangeriiine.'

Clem the Bet threw me a look like the clown who hadn't been paid by Billy Smarts circus for the last five custard pie fights. Hitting daylight, we pushed Boney toward a quiet back-alley. Within its confines a two-pronged attack began. I only got the first dig in because I was shouting louder than Paddy. 'What the fuck are you up to? You daft, golliwog-headed-twat! Here's us loaded up with gear and we've gorra search the fucken streets for you!'

Paddy added. 'First you bring us all to the point of capture by bellowing our names all over the street, instead of keeping you're gob shut and taking the chase yourself. Then you go on one of your Aboriginal walkabouts with the swagbag. Fucksake Boney, wake up lad, you're gonna get us all nicked!'

'Alright! Alright! Take it easy will yer? I was only having a bet!'

Stuffing lifted gear into the swagbag, I'm telling him, 'You should've been a mime artist or a street painter, like your daft mate Tanger-fucken-rine, then you could've opted out of the real world and stayed in the betting Office with all the other horse' n' jockey dreamers!'

Overstating the point, I carried on in the same vein. 'Yeah, I can just see it. Roll up, roll up, come on you generous people, dig deep and put some money towards this man's next bet, as I present to you, Boney, the blind-eyed Juggler. Gamble on which skittle he might catch, or, meanwhile, why don't you get your portrait painted by Mr. Boney Rolf Maloney; every picture a messed-up masterpiece; a hashed-up fucken Hockney to hang over the mantelpiece. Get me drift shithead? Wake the fuck up will yer!

Ok, I was going on a bit, but if Boney didn't catch drift, Paddy sure did. Informing him he'd best join the wide-awake club was the Cuban-heel-over-the-head way of telling him we were all going straight to jail, Monopoly style, if he didn't liven up. But, it was his persona, and you could hit him on the head with whatever you liked, all it would succeed in doing was dimming the light bulb even more. He was a mate though, wasn't he, you know, thick as thieves an' all that. Anthony was a Mersey Aborigine mate at that, and, I have to say Anthony, because it sounds so fucken droll when you say Tony Boney Maloney or, just Tony Maloney; sort of drippy-Irish, or like a sausage'd-up-Italian meal. Boney and pale-white in frame, curly and jet-black in wig and just above dunce school level in knowledge ability; dozy-hole normally only got called Anthony by his loving mother. Once the two-pronged attack had stopped, he shouted 'Don't you mean a Cockney?'

'Yer what?'

'You said a hashed-up fucken Hockney. Cheek – calling me dim, it's a Cockney, not a Hockney!'

I looked at Paddy, he looked at me; we both looked at Boney and burst out laughing.

Paddy wouldn't go near a betting office; not unless there was a sexy kitten marking the boards inside, that is. He wouldn't waste his money on horses, but he'd spend every last penny chasing a new bit of fluff. All fashion, records and sparkly ladies, an' that sort of stuff. An English city centre, Saturday, shopping boy and a lad's lad with knobs on. Dressed sharp and flirting in all the right gaffs. Shops, pubs, clubs, you name it. In the know, on the go, always spending dough! Essential when you're young, I suppose.

Bounding the streets as kids, with his boots, braces and button-down Ben Sherman's, he'd been the first little Suedehead to walk the walk. That'd be late sixties, early seventies. Come the mid to late seventies, first with a wedge haircut, straight-leg jeans and college shoes. He was a fair-haired, council estate smoothie, the sweetshop burglar supreme – the Rebel without a door key. The fussy little stud was so particular about his threads that he'd only wear mid 1980s gear to go Hoisting in, you know, so as to not look suspicious. He despised that lacey New Romantic shit and all those Thatcherite double breasted power suits. One time, coming out of The Bank tube station, after graft, he had me in bulk when we got chased upstairs by the Underground Clippy, when he shouted 'I'm not paying for another Spandau Ballet haircut for the likes of you!'

The guard had one of those lacquered-up Billy Fury type barnets and was asking for the correct fare after we'd given him some out of date tickets. On London lifting days he wore a waxed Barbour jacket like a second skin. 'The greatest shop-lifting coats ever invented' he'd say; though, I'm sure the hunting fraternity would disagree. But boy did that kid look like Yuppiedom personified as he strolled down New Bond Street on the prowl. If Boney was a dozy Koala bear, Paddy was another English street shark. Funny, but still a shark!

The majority of the girls we bumped into never looked past Patrick McArdle. Few drinks, loosened up and fully-flush and everybody got a drink. Not only generous when he'd downed a few, it also seemed to bring his good points to the fore; unlike some touchy tipplers who can become a right pain

in the pink rosette after a whisky teardrop. A strong resemblance to James Dean was another advantage in Paddy's pulling
technique; especially when he deep-blued the females while
flashing the cash. Any trouble with girls or twirls and he had
one of the most notorious Liverpool families to back him up.
His mad uncle Tommy had a name weight equivalent to a
Sherman tank. Paddy knew this, but never threw out the name
or abused its strength.

Me, Mickey Mac, I was usually happy with the leftovers
after smooth-balls had gorged himself on young London
lovelies. I mean, I could say unequivocally that if one kid ever
over-dosed on buttered cockney crumpet then this was the
press-up king of the North; our own dirty ticket, yeah, jack' o
the lads.

The three of us, slum-clearance kids, had been shoved out
of the city centre to a brand-new Council Estate, come
overspill, built six miles outside of the Northern city of
Liverpool. Tenements no longer in view, it was all forests and
fields for us; so we took to nature with a crowbar in one hand
and a permanently upturned two fingers on the other. Being
crowbar kids, we'd spend our time spray-painting trees,
collecting bird's eggs and forever fighting with the jolly-green-
farmers whose fields ran adjacent to the railway tracks.
Normally they'd be shaking their jowls over a few carrots or
spuds we'd taken; bunch of land-grabbing tight-arses! Mind
you, it was no joke for Farmer Buckshot to have Paddy sniffing
around his daughter's knicker-elastic. Me, I'd have been happy
with a sniff round the belly-warmers of his Norah Batty of a
wife.

Traipsing the countryside surrounding our new community, discovering new factories led to burgling new
factories, and the untimely arrival of the Bizzies led to a few
uncomfortable lie-downs at the local Police Station. First visit:
large, leather-clad, steel toe-cap, met small and lean, raggedy
bum-cheek as a cell door welcome. One too many visits to the

same Plod Shop, meant leather-clad knuckle met urchin cheekbone as a front door greeting. Greeting then meeting the leather clout of the brutal desk Sergeant became an occupational, gloved-up hazard for our mob; especially one time when young Boney neglected lookout duties by falling asleep on the sweet factory roof.

It was something those store-detectives never did, you know, fall asleep on guard duty. Mind you, probably blend better if they did. Those cardboard cutouts were, and still are, the walking billboards of shopping-aisles. Hanging about goods on offer like cerise pink, four-litre Corvettes, but, never able to move like one. Nothing in common with a chameleon those useless retail-plod; standing there like john Lennon's Piano in a Coal Yard, staring through gaps in shelving trying to make you believe they're shopping just like you. Never the champions of in-store hide' n' seek, eh, you serial walkers of the floor. Don't you think it's about time you got your bleeding act together? This is after all, the new millennium an' all that.

Anyway, minor Floorwalker details; leave them to catch pensioners an' that. Come on, we've had Florida rattle, Hoisters rattle, growing up and meaning of life rattle. No more of that for now. Now that I've given you a little taste of what we were up to, let's leave all that stuff for a bit and find out why this lifting lark kicked-off in the first place. I'd like to take you on a little Hoisting trip with me; a sort of sharp, penniless kid, on a journey towards a blunt, well-heeled, adult destination. It's a trip where you can easily lose track; some would say like me, or simply lose the plot, like other rag-arses trying to battle their way out of Skintville. Join me, on a light-fingered journey around most of the modern World and, if the on-pier skaters continue to leave me in peace, I'll try to take you smoothly through the checkouts and security gates that supposedly lead to the land of milk and money.

My light fingered account can only open in one place, with an instant withdrawal from the bank of knowledge. A lesson learnt early about the crossing of swords with establishment figures; namely: those fellows of the mighty Masonic Lodge, with their funny handshakes, their shady, late night meetings and their covering up of dirty deeds committed by their beloved brethren. Well fellers, I suppose you're the pinstripe suits driving the tasty BMW's down the fast lane of life's highway – it's happening again, I mean, motorway – with the rest of us meanwhile, still chugging over those bumpy country lanes in our John and Sue Ford Escorts. But, watch out boys, check the fella getting road rage in the inside lane, could be me, and you never know, mine just might be the swag-laden GTI version.

3

WHEN THE TIGERS BROKE FREE

Steel to Steal – Dock Road Liverpool mid 1980's

'**C**an you answer the phone Mr. Johnson?'
No sign of wrinkly old Sid James
when you need him.

'Mr. Johnson…can you answer the phone please?'

The daft old bleeder's probably fell asleep again. I'm dealing with a customer at the counter window of a small steel stockholder. It's an office within a warehouse, where people walk in to place an order for angle iron, RSJ's and any type steel, for whatever purpose in mind. I've already answered two phones and left both people hanging on the line. A third phone rings. It's the same every lunch hour, soon as somebody shoots out for a nosebag the phones kick-off. I've got one of those Big Time Charlie customers in a hurry, as per usual.

'Come on Mickey lad, big jobs broke out; got to get the steel before we do the deal.'

Big time Charlie's identity bracelet hangs like a bog-chain from his wrist, dangling and jangling on the steel counter. He'd told me a number of times he had something to do with boat building; small mind you, even though he spoke like he was Mr. fucking Cammell Laird himself. I joked to him. 'Hope the new boat's not gonna sink, can't see it taking the weight of you and you're ID bracelet?'

41

He grunted some sort of acknowledgement. Big Time, like the other movers and shakers you'd see standing impatiently at the window, never registered any real joy unless he was on the make or take. A Pure and utter Bread-head didn't speak to you – even attempting a joke – they spoke at you. Big time, truly born under the pound sign, offered advice. 'No time for laughter and jokes in this game son!'

Judging by his tatty-head, barbed-wire-fringe and jungle scene Hawaiian shirt, no time for a wash, shave, or trip down the menswear department neither then eh! Demanding my *full* attention, I called for help. 'Mr. Johnson, any chance of answering the phone please?'

Only two weeks ago a Managing Director had paid a visit. First thing on the agenda was lack of staff during the busy lunch hour period. It was agreed old Mr. Johnson had to leave his small office to help with window enquiries and ringing phones. Only needed at lunch hour, the rest of the time he could laze about on his crinkle-cut, bum cheeks, planning his holidays, reading smut mags, and doing whatever it took to while away the hours, days and weeks before retirement in two years.

I'm thinking, *third phone's bound to stop ringing, I'll leave it.* Whoever rang eventually gave up. Ringing over, Jolly Johnson came steaming out of his smoke filled office. 'Why didn't you answer that call?'

Oh, so he did hear it, did he?

'Well, as you can see, I've got two phones on the go and Barry's Boats at the window, in a hurry as usual.'

'Never mind all that. Your job is to serve customers and answer phones. That could have been an important sale.'

Meantime, Mr. Bojangles, rattling his identity bracelet on the counter, added loud tuts to his impatient rattle. Twat of a man!

'But Mr. Johnson, Max Armitage said the other day you'd be helping out if it got really bad during lunch-break.'

'Never mind what Maxwell Armitage said. While I'm here, you do as I say, and I'm telling you to make sure that those bloody phones get answered!'

And off he toddled to his smoking den and his library of European road maps. See, Sid James Johnson, the Mr. Carry-on-Camping of the Dock Road, liked to plan driving breaks around Austria and Germany in one of those big caravanette's, blagging his wrinkly, old teabag of a wife, how he'd love to get away with her for a short-break. All the time he probably only planned to retrace the tank tracks of his Nazi war heroes.

I'm getting seriously wound up by now. Apart from the obvious lack of co-operation from Carry-on Sid, the statement by Max Armitage about old Johnno helping out had been prompted by me, due to no senior staff having the bottle to bring the matter up themselves. Bunch of ladder climbing jobsworths, what can you do? By now, this lunch-hour lark was becoming all too frequent an occurrence. Giving a quick 'hold the line' to the two callers hanging on, I started serving the Bracelet, only for the third phone to start ringing all over again.

Shit! I'm thinking, continue serving Barry's boat full of bracelet's, or answer the phone. Phone – Bracelet – Bracelet – Phone? Looking over Bracelets barbed-wire bonce, out toward the yard, showed nobody returning from lunch. We had two wagon drivers and two warehouse labourers who'd sometimes help out in the office. No sign of any of them. Phone – Bracelet – Bracelet – Phone? Aarrgh! Fuck this! 'Mr. Johnson, Mr. Johnson, can you answer the phone please?'

Not a dickybird!

'MR. JOHNSON…HELLO-HO!'

Shouting at the top of my voice, Bracelet's covered his ears to avoid the din. The thick, gold, bog chain rides down one arm as he raises both hands to his ears.

'Hello, Steel Stockholders, hold the line please.'

Picking up the two other phones simultaneously, I repeat, 'Hello, Steel Stockholders hold the line please.'

A voice comes back at me from one of the phones. 'No, I won't hold the line, and shove a piece of angle iron up yer fucken arse!'

He hung up. You have to sympathize with the guy, he's been holding on a while now. Without any callback or trace on the line, he could be as offensive and as vulgar as he wanted, with no chance of comeback.

No sooner I replaced the receiver than it started ringing again. 'Hello, Steel Stockholders, hold the line please.'

Another guy arrived at the window; enough is enough. Approaching Jolly Johnson's smoking den, I opened the door. There he sat in his own little bunker, reading his Gateway to the Third Reich maps; all the while dreaming about 1940's Germany and Eva Braun stroking Adolf's prawn.

'What is it?' He growled, in a heavy, Lancastrian, mill-town accent; nonchalantly looking up from his Nazi route planner.

'You'll have to come and help at the counter…or the phones; it's mad busy!'

'What did I tell you lad? You'll have to deal with it yourself; are you deaf or something?'

Well, it was the 'deaf' bit that finally triggered my spud gun. 'Deaf you say, Deaf! I've been shouting at the top of my voice for you to answer one of those bloody phones!'

'Don't you take that tone with me lad; do you hear? How dare you take that *bloody* tone with me?'

'Tone,' I'm saying, 'Tone. The only tone round here is you, Mr. Tone Bloody Deaf!'

He looked shocked. 'You'll be out on your backside in no time at all young man if you keep using that voice with me.'

'At least if I go out on my arse, I'll have an arse to go out on. Yours is probably worn down to the bone, seeing as you're always putting you're full weight on it!'

'That's it! You're for the sack…Mister Bloody know it all!'

'Sack, sack, the only sack around here is you, you oul' sack of shit!!'

The sack of shit jibe was like playing the joker in 'Join the Dole-Queue, it's a Knockout'. This part of the game show was called The Breakneck to Benefit Race, where my well played sack of shit taunt just gained me instant double points.

A lot of false promises were made when I started selling steel under the sleepy gaze of Sid James, promises of further advancement within a short period of time, more staff employed so the workload did not become intolerable, and, more important to my mind, a supposed wage hike after a three-month trial period. None of these materialized, leaving me with a bitter taste and a mother and father under volcanic eruption orders, seeing as their blue-eyed was about to add himself to the already burgeoning dole queue numbers.

Few days later, fed up listening to Floyd and Bunnymen albums in record stores, I went back to pick up my severance pay. Family remained none-the-wiser about my unemployed status. I knew I'd have to Stanley knife the illusion sooner or later, as leaving the house at eight in the morning for a nine hour walkabout couldn't be sustained over a long period of time. See, I wasn't up for explaining anything to family at that moment. A bit of a hullabaloo had been made when I first got the job, and, here I was, a year down the line, sacked and ready to return to Planet Couch. Oh well, time to face Sid and the Carry on crew; fuck-it! Here goes. Entering the gates, I was surprised to see Max Armitage. Time for tonsils. 'Hello Max, do you have a moment?'

Way up the ladder in terms of seniority, Max seemed amiable enough and a whole lot easier to talk to than old man Johnson. The two came from totally opposite backgrounds. Max: old-school-tie brigade, an academic man with public school education. He'd married into the company years ago and probably hadn't had to kiss brown eye to get to where he was today. Other side of the Masons apron, old Johnno: working class through and through, from his shiny, polyester suits to his strangle-you're-lung Woodbine cigarettes.

Intrinsically linked by their Handshake Harry connections, they'd reached their position in life by similar means; similar, but not the same. Max, as I've said, could be amiable, even sociable, and you're talking about a time when a lot of working class people could be wary of, or even intimidated by, a six-foot something, sharply dressed and spoken, ex-Public schoolboy. Bit of a Michael Portillo of the shop-floor...hmm, maybe? Old man Johnno meanwhile, was a gruff Northern Lancastrian: cynical, high-handed, jaded and lazy; the last I grant, probably due to old age. He had a face like that fella Benny Hill used to slap on the head all the time. Yeah, you bet I was tempted!

Max offered me a chair. 'Sit down Mickey. Now what's this entire rumpus about? You know it's not too late. A simple written apology will suffice. Mr. Johnson will be retiring in two years; hang-fire. Get your head down to the same standard of work you've been producing and I'm sure you'll have a bright future ahead of you.'

'But Max, when you interviewed me for this job a year ago, a lot of promises got made about job prospects and so forth. The Company has completely reneged on all of those objectives...as far as I can see.'

I'm thinking, *Mmmm, not bad, that came out quite well;* which was instantly followed by a little vision of my Ma and Da jointly screaming at me, *'JUST WRITE THE APOLOGY DICKHEAD!'*

Without wishing to sound all Nostradamus, I honestly knew the moment would remain a defining one for me. Nine to five safety, button your lip, and like Pink Floyd had said, *'Welcome my son, welcome to the Machine'*, or, open your gob, tell it like it is and find your own way round the planet! Max, sensing how far-reaching a decision I had to make, looked me in the eye. 'Have a few minutes, take your time. I personally would like you to stay. I took you on because I thought you showed potential to move quickly upward within this company. Putting aside your little spat with Mr. Johnson, I've yet to be proved wrong.'

Pushing things forward a little, before he left the room, I said, 'and no possibility of Mr. Johnson being moved to a different branch or...being pensioned off early...err, I suppose?'

Max closed the door gently and replied in a somewhat annoyed manner, as though I wasn't getting the message. 'No son. No chance! We've known for a long time now that Mr. Johnson has been idling away towards retirement; deadwood, if you'd like me to speak bluntly. But he's been with us...for... going on twenty years, and I suppose we now count him as one of our own. And with just two years to go, you do realize we have to look after our own. I'm sure you can agree on that. Listen, you sit tight. I've no doubt your day will come...Have a few moments, nothing rash. Think things over. Give me a nod when you're ready; if not, I'll be back soon.'

Almost a year ago to the day, I'd returned home with my tail between my legs after learning a severe lesson in life's realities. Big wages beckoned from the building sites of Germany so, along with the brother and his trowel we beamed ourselves down to Frankfurt; finding out quickly, the usual clichéd version of Johnny Foreigner and his country didn't stand up. The naive picture we'd painted of Deutschland brimming with thousands of square headed, sausage-eaters, all happily doing the Goose-step to work, got quickly buried in concrete beneath the first set of footings we dug.

Four weeks into my Auf Wiedersehen learning curve, a dwarf-like Birmingham site agent upped sticks with half the sites wages – mine included. I'd shifted serious German soil on my way to those Deutsch Marks, so when they weren't forthcoming, the steel toe cap end of the learning curve left me badly bruised. The brother and I, along with ten Geordies, ten other Liverpudlians and four lads from Salford, swore the first person to meet up with the Elton John lookalike from Walsall, would do everything within capability to topple the Brummie midget off his six-inch Cuban-heels, before performing a full Air Wair boot to brain execution. It could've turned into a case of chasing the Rocket-man up the Rhine, if any of us caught a glimpse of the four foot ten conman.

With my two brothers back on the Dole, my Da: unemployed and blacklisted after being on one too many picket lines, my Ma: a dinner lady working for a pittance, and me: the boy wonder, still in the good books till further notice, now I'd just been given notice, the message from family came loud and clear. 'WRITE THE APOLOGY DICKHEAD!'

Max clearly wanted me to stay, but making my own choice was what mattered here. Two years of sitting tight, clobber stinking of Woodbines every day, listening to Sid James' tar infested lungs going, in-out, in-out as he starred in his own 'Carry-on-Smoking-till-death' movie. Two years! Two whole years! I didn't fancy two more fucking days pandering to old saggy bollocks!

Surprised they were ready to give me another chance after lips shifted gear, though it had taken months to pluck up the courage to speak my mind, I knew I'd overstepped the mark between boss and dogsbody. Saying that, I also knew any more looking-down-your-nose-at-me-shit, from Benny Hill's slap-head, could result in an even angrier response. Last thing I wanted was old prune features keeling over mid-argument. The whole workforce knew he had a dodgy ticker, same as we knew the Handshake Harry's ran the company and, due to naivety about all matters Masonic, I thought it might result in either a severe docklands beating one night after work, or worse, I'd be beating my Da by at least twenty five years in getting onto the jobs blacklist.

Being unsure about the power and influence the Masons exerted, I had England's Masonic Mafia as the UK version of the American Cosa Nostra. Not to dissimilar an organization, when you think the hand-signed English firm had power and friends in high places, and the hands-on Italian-American mob had power and...friends in high places. Pie and mash, spaghetti and meatball, handshake versus Uzi; serious thinking was needed here... and fast!

Looking at the five working years I'd had since school, there had been a four year apprenticeship promise, ending in redundancy after one, six months on the dole, which bored me shitless, and, if anything, it gave my poverty stricken, light-fingered tendencies time to develop. Then, I was off. Getting kicked onto the dole, one year into my Electricians apprentice-ship, was the catalyst and kick-start my Hoisting apprenticeship needed. Sort of, Devil finds work for idle but eager hands palaver. Trying to nip any bad habits, I knew were forming, in the bud, I skedaddled off for an Aboriginal working walkabout in Australia for one year. Here, two Australian customs officials – border patrol for the original convict's island, paid to keep the new law breakers out – noticing (after a snitch's tip-off) that I'd overstayed my welcome with an out of date work permit, ordered two beefy, Ozz-cops to frog-march me back to an airport holding cell. Once my opinionated gob opened wide, the two large, medium-rare, kangaroo steaks – playing Ozz-rules – tried drop-kicking me all the way back to Blighty, getting as far as Melbourne airport in the process.

I mean, two Merv Hughes, Melbourne macho's, with tashes to match; what is it with coppers and hairy top-lips? Four jobs, and nearly a year later, I flew homeward through fluffy English clouds for a Christmas drink. For the long flight home my face carried its own piece of tanned luggage: a red snooker ball nose; the first in a long line of snooker ball noses. My brother said it was fitting I'd returned during the season of goodwill, as my shiny conk twinned me with Rudolph. What he didn't know, was Rudolph's twin had found the Australians were not giving any 'stuff' away, and that a long line of convict ancestry had left them wise to any shop shenanigans the young red-nosed, redneck might've undertaken.

Lifting earners in Oz were a definite non-starter, with shopkeeper's peepers resembling glass eyes on springs. Hardly any eucalyptus chomping Floorwalkers could be found *doing the detective*, amid Aussie department store floors. Keen as surf grease the bastards were; Koala bears, they were not. Like a logged-on gang of beach surfing, store detectives, with shelves doubling up as waves; up, down, up, down, bobbing up to the top shelf and weaving back down the aisles, waiting for the big shoplifter's wipeout, they loved their job like other Aussies loved cricket. But, like Arnie had said and, like the eventual killer wave, I'd be back. I didn't know it at the time, but it was grade A homework to put toward the big shoplifting O' level and, sure as shops is shops, one day 'stuff from down under' would help towards my bigger freedom plan. They'd soon have to tie those kangaroos down alright!

Two months back in the land of not-a-hope-of-any-glory, and a cold British winter gave me the urge to try the South African lifestyle. I stayed there for roughly a year and a half. It could easily have been two weeks, when I realized I'd gone back in time to Nazi Germany; but, I never had the required dough to make a hasty return. I'm glad I stayed longer now; the place was such a cultural eye opener. Those white-skinned, Boer boys, with their prejudiced, political agenda of early 1980s South Africa, brought home to me the meaning of the word BIGOTRY. Meanwhile, although the dogmatic Dutch descendents made Thatcher and her Home county Henchmen look like a bunch of young, farty-arsed Liberal students, it still didn't make me hate those blinkered Tory Bastards back home any less!

Considering the twenty odd years I'd been flesh and blood, the bottom bit of Africa at that time felt so far detached from my socialist upbringing that, living among a gang of Fascist penguins in the North Pole, or sharing an igloo amid the Antarctic ice sheets with Mussolini couldn't have felt any further from mother country. I have to be careful here, Max was looking for an answer soon, and I could easily go off on one just thinking about the weird things that were happening in White' n' Right South Africa around the early eighties. Don't know if its minor details again? Sod it, here's a brief.

Johannesburg's posh suburbs of Sandton and Randburg were routinely paid a visit. With me donning the favoured coloured skin, my freckled, paleface complexion left me with acres of shop-floor space to further indulge my Hoisting tendencies. It also left me with shopping-bags-full-of-time to continually top-up my lifting education. Left completely alone in the stores, any hidden security cameras might've had me down as back store ghost. Working as a roofer or bricklayer's labourer midweek, around the wealthy white suburbs of Jo'burg, I often crossed to the other side of the tracks to work in dirt-poor townships like Alexandria and Soweto; places that let me know the huge difference between penniless and poverty stricken and being hungry or truly starving. Saturdays, plus the odd day off, I spent further exploring the shifty eyed, cloak and dagger world of light fingered Larry. The Floorwalkers of South Africa were only interested in clocking the destitute natives, not a fair-haired Boer Boy they had me down as; leaving me to get on with my new apprenticeship in peace.

My Electrical apprenticeship, cut short by redundancy, I knew the natural way for this apprenticeship to end would be in prison. I learned about Robben Island jail off the Cape Town coast: a political slammer where the Whitey's could lock up people like Nelson Mandela and throw away the key. Me, being a whitey, small time lifter, I'd be sent to a Yarpie Yard in Jo'burg or Pretoria for a few months kip. If they'd have dealt out a fraction of Mandela's treatment to all rule-breakers, and I'd have found out about it, I wouldn't have touched a fucken Mars Bar wrapper!

Though young, I was well aware of Jo'burgs glut of diamonds. The old trick of replacing an expensive beauty back in the tray of rings with a cheap, shitty fake, left me in receivership of a few sparklers that a friendly Indian fence paid the usual third for – in Rand mind you – two to the pound at the time, leaving me wedged-up and ready to go. Each day on the long, uphill walk home from work to Hillbrow, a high-rise concrete jungle packed with immigrants nearby the city centre, a black Sowetan street hustler, risking a heavy jail sentence on a daily basis, stopped people on their way home from the city, to try and entice them into buying one of the huge diamond rings he'd show and tell you he'd recently relieved from a jewellers window display. 'Hot as hell this treasure. Got to sell now,' was how he put it – if you looked gullible enough!

He must have thought me a nice, gullible whitey, as he accosted me on the pavement every day of every week. Anyone with a decent glass eye could see they were duds so, I bought three for fifty Rand, a big come down from the six hundred he'd started bidding at. He told me his name was Emanuel. I thought of the soft porn movies from back home. True or not, I never got to know. One true thing that arose from our brief encounter was that the fakes did end up in a Jewish jewellers window display after all. Within a week – dressing smart, playing the part – I'd planted Emanuel's dud sparklers in three different jewellery stores, in exchange for three Jo'burg beauties the Indian fence snaffled up hungrily – paying accordingly.

I finally come unstuck on the right-on, right-wing one day, when too long spent at the back of a huge DIY store soon found me walking through checkout in possession of a coat full of tools, on yet another hot, sunny, South African day. Laziness on my behalf set off a security device attached to a builders' spirit level I hadn't checked. Instantly pursued over surrounding fields by five to ten shop staff, the chase was on. Diving under a barbed wire fence bordering the local motorway, my shirt got tangled in spiky wire after I'd lashed a tool-laden, cumbersome coat. Pounced upon by two guards who could've passed as the George Foreman twins, my new entourage led me back to the DIY superstore.

Re-entering the place it suddenly transformed, in my eyes, to a tool hire shop...well, I had to think of something, didn't I. It was obvious from who was doing all the ordering and talking, who was boss. Old Whitey, blonde and blue eyed, like me, told the guards to ease off with the manhandling, giving me hope.

Reaching Whitey's office, back of the store, he dismissed the George Foreman twin's and closed the door. 'Why, oh why, oh why?' he remarked, before adding in that accent that always reminds me of a far-right, Afrikaner, Boer boy. 'You must have a real good reason and need, to be stealing tools like these?'

He was a poet who didn't know it. The tough, angular faces of the Springbok rugby team stared up at me from a framed picture on his desk. A couple of the slyer looking ones seemed to be giving me the beady eye; either that or they were smirking at the rhyme same as me. Getting rid of my feint smile – pronto – I rapidly forgot about the rooms minor details as he asked my name. I'd hardly finished my surname when he almost leapt from his chair to lecture me about the type of example we should be setting to the native Africans and, how stealing just wasn't the white, Christian thing to do. Though it was me on shop trial, I couldn't get a word in edgeways.

Old Whitey, the preacher, eyes magnified by the glass ashtrays he wore, eventually paused from his sermon for breath. As I nervously spoke, he butted straight in again, asking what circumstances led me to feel so desperate I was ready to steal tools for work. Well...the circumstances that brought me to this DIY store, in this country...now, that was a long, long story. But, the circumstances that led me to the story I was about to tell Whitey, well, hmm...that was a lot more superficial and could always be improvised or added to. He'd shown his true colour and plain distaste of the black population, and had clearly let me know we sat in his office on the same side of the colour bar; like we were mates on the same Springbok team, or something, and I'd just made an unfortunate manoeuvre or pass he might be able to juggle or rectify. It was a chance to get past the handcuffs. That's it. He'd given me green light, shaded with white. I was off.

Telling him I'd arrived at Jan Smuts airport from Northern Britain, cold, young and alone, I'd waited for a lovely, white, non-existent relative to pick me up outside the terminal building. While hanging about my 'fresh air' tools had been stolen by two invisible, yet shady looking black men. After paying for a flight and a month's rent with borrowed money, and my last unemployment handout, quickly in-collar, my first South African boss had let me know that having my own tools on site was a must. Looking into my saddened misty blues, Old Whitey took in the gory-glory-story for a moment. 'But why didn't you get a loan to pay for some new ones?'

'Well, I already owe money to family back home, for giving me the chance to get to South Africa in the first place.'

'Those bloody Kaffir's: thieving black barstards all of them. You mean you borrowed money to come all the way here for work?'

'Yeah'

As he hopped aboard the chin rubbing train of thought, I wandered why his accent made a bastard sound like a bar stud, a man who pulled all the birds at the local boozer, and what the fuck a Kaffir was?

'My-oh-my-oh-my, that is a sad story. And I must say, although I can't condone stealing in any way, I think in your circumstances an exception should be made for the commendable effort you have shown in getting here, and, in trying to get yourself to work...Bloody Kaffir's eh; might've known!'

Sitting there, starry eyed and stunned, trying to work out what Kaffir stood for, he unbelievably went on to offer me a job at the same rate of pay I supposedly earned on site, adding that, in my present situation, it was in some ways admirable what I had done. Tempted to take his offer – he sure sounded like a fair boss to work for, if you were white that is – the guilt and shame of looking my pursuers in the eye every day at work soon smothered that notion. When I declined, he amazingly let me keep the tools I'd stolen, as long as I promised to come back and pay when my pockets were flush with Rand. My only sentence for the crime committed: I had to make a second promise I would keep in touch on this, the same day, every month, for one year; just to let Old Whitey know I was progressing in his beautiful country and light fingered no more.

The fairness and honesty he'd shown, allied to biasness toward skin, had me seriously dumbfounded. My rapid descent into becoming a devious Jackanory storyteller left me unnerved and feeling guilty – bit like the boy who cried wolf had just robbed a bag of tools. Trying to save conscience, I wondered if he'd have applied the same set of standards to a young black kid caught in the act. I thought not. I called on Old Whitey to pay for the tools, then with progress reports, letting him believe I was turning into a good ol' Boer-boy since landing on African soil. The more I saw of him with those magnified eyes, the more he reminded me of Hank Marvin from the Shadows. But, once he tried pointing that a certain passage from the Bible told of how the black man was born to serve the white man, my suspicions he was just another South African crank 'deceiving' not playing in the shadows, were confirmed. I started ringing with excuses I was busy in work, and eventually stopped ringing altogether. Even though he'd given me an honest second chance, I'd found his honesty and demeanor too good to be true. There's always a Billy goat of a butt with honesty that direct isn't there?

Work permits out of date, the continual illegal alien, fed up worrying about his little stash under the bed at his rough Hillbrow flat, decided to return home from Fascistburg, South

Africa on the first flight out of Jan Smuts airport. On the crap TAP, Air Portugal flight back to Heathrow, you're looking at Mr. Jack-of-all-trades, master of none, sitting there on a postage stamp size seat with fifteen thousand South African Rand stuffed down his undies. The underpants got packed with banknotes because right wing legislation meant the right wing Rozzers were empowered to stop anybody leaving the country with any money they didn't know about – like my sparklers money for instance.

Economy bucket seat, allied to stuffed undies and being scared of a money fall out, meant I hardly budged for the thirteen hour flight duration. I was okay, my arteries pumped too fast to become an early deep-vein-thrombosis casualty, and my willy was still young and powerful enough to hold its juice for more than a few hours. Rand changed to sterling, and blew; brief stint of charity work for a Brummie Elton John in Frankfurt, time wasted; English social security number, back in place; this once illegal alien, legal once more, now sat arse-parked in the offices of a Liverpool steel stockholders with a life determining decision to make.

Max came back in. 'Have you written the apology Mickey?'

Wanting to tell him to stick his job up his pinstriped bottom cheeks – sideways – I resisted the urge. He'd never been that bad to me, except for empty promises and, I mean, show me a boss on the planet that doesn't make those.

'No Max, no apologies. The only man who should be making any apologies is the lazy old man out there in the warehouse; treating and talking to me like a fucken slave!'

The final F word cut the 9 to 5 umbilical cord with as much sensitivity as a Kung Fu Master chopping at a breeze block! With no more lifelines on offer, he passed me my severance pay and told me to direct any future references to his main office in Blackburn.

Weaving my way out of the building through rusty lengths of steel, I said my goodbyes to ex-colleagues. They seemed genuinely sorry to see me go. Outside, old man Johnson was checking a wagonload of steel before the driver left on deliveries. Trying to blank me, I went to give him a mouthful. I thought better of it. Looking at him, I realized that that could've been me in forty years. Being blunt, I hoped more for a Des O'Connor look later in life than a prune-like Sid James. Ok, Des looked like he was coated in fresh dog shit, but at least he didn't look like year old dog shit!

Thinking that was that, end of story, Ronnie the wagon driver caught me up. 'Mickey, It's gonna start raining, d'yer wanna lift?'

'Nah, it's okay Ronnie, I'm gonna take a stroll into town.'

The heavens were about to cave but, in my own strange way I willed the rain to start pissing down all over the shitty clobber I was wearing. Walking along the Mersey sea front, I loved the freedom, fresh air and the rain. I always found a type of solitude in its bleakness; a place where drift-off came easy. The daydream: the one where I'd tell my Ma and Da how one day the big ship would come and take me away to New York, never to return. A dream I shared with hundreds of other Liverpool kids. I'd settle in the land of opportunity and become a big-truck, before sending for family once I'd made a name for mys...'Mickey! Mickey!' Ronnie the driver was shouting me.

'Mickey, d'yer wanna lift or what?'

'Nah, it's alright Ronnie.'

'Anyway, its best yer leaving; that oul bastard had it in for you.'

'How d'yer mean like?'

'Well, the Maxi fella has been asking around the yard, if anyone thinks the fiddle is down to you.'

'Why the fuck would he do that then?'

'Oul Johnno apparently put it into his head. But it doesn't matter now does it?'

Ignoring anything else he had to say, I dashed straight back to the warehouse.

'MIIICKEEY, DON'T TELL THEM I TOLD YEH!'

'Shut the fuck up Ronnie lad,' I'm saying to myself out loud. Who else are they going to think told me? The drivers had been taking a few lengths of steel each day for the past six months, since the yearly profits had been announced, which were more than healthy but didn't show up in our pay packets. The drivers earned Soweto wages, in my view. Maybe Central London government thought Liverpool was a township? Anyway, I fully understood the little fiddle they'd set-up. However, setting it up had nothing to do with me; except maybe the fact I'd turned a blind-eye.

The old red mist fast-extinguished any clear thought. Composing myself, I had to choose words carefully. It was imperative I didn't give the two suits any more reason to be glad they were rid of me. Stereotypical stuff, like 'little guttersnipe from the council estate' and any other cheap parceling labels, I couldn't take. I'm thinking, *watch the language son; watch the language.* Before contradicting myself, *hang on, I'm conversing with a couple of fellers who've spent most of their working lives on northern industrial estates; fuck worrying about the P's and Q's!*

Opening the warehouse door I found Max Armitage and the old bastard having a con-flab. Old Johnno bent slightly as he tried to clean mud from his brand new Hush Puppies. The suede shoes looked like two hamsters about to run through the steel. Approaching from behind I was tempted to take a free kick with his polyester bum cheeks but stopped when I noticed how wrinkly his neck was. Jesus, I'd been taking orders from a turtle for the past year. Still talking, I butted in. 'Did you tell Max that the missing steel was down to me by any chance?'

No answer.

'Did you mention that I was involved in any 'fiddling'?'

No answer.

'Max, has this senile old fart said anything untoward about

me? Ah forget it! I see, the brethren closing ranks eh...Is that what this is?' You...are...pathetic...and I mean the pair of yer.'

The Turtles' neck came out an inch from its green Polyester shell. 'Did you say pathetic? Pathetic! I went through a bloody world war for the likes of you, sonny. How dare you!'

At last, an answer. Zapping a raw nerve, the turtle had left its shell to take the bait. I was flowing. 'World war – Ha! Don't make me laugh. The closest you probably got to fighting in the war was working as a medic in the T.A!'

The older drivers told me about old Johnno giving it the big war hero story, after senior management figures had told them at a pre-Christmas tipple, with tongues loosened, that he'd never seen a battle in his life. National service – yes, battles – only with his missus and co-workers fed up with his laziness. Filthy old blagger!

Max, struggling to suppress laughter, brought a hand to his mouth, imitating a cough. It was a waste of time trying to get my message across, but I couldn't resist a last pop. 'For what it's worth Max, all the staff can't stand working under ol' lazy bollocks there. I'm just the first person to let you know. If you want a happier more productive workforce then you've gorra two-year on-going problem to deal with. Anyway, yer know I'm right, so ta-ta for now.'

Chirping up, sounding nonchalant and carefree, I turned to walk out. Really, I was churning inside, thinking how I'd like to take a year of grief out on the turtles head. Airing a few grievances had released some red mist, while instinct told me manhandling wasn't the right way to end things. Closing the Warehouse door, an eerie feeling swept over me. It intensified when I was greeted by monsoon like rain dancing all over the docks...Splish splash I was taking a bath.

An urban wasteland assault course – Liverpool's Dock Road – lay in front of me. I'm thinking, *here we go*. Like any fit, young lad who'd been locked in a stinking ten by ten office all day, I started running wildly, and jumping accordingly. Slow at first, then faster...Faster...FASTER!

Speeding the mile and a half into town, I purposely jumped into any fresh rain pools the road had to offer. An old discarded three piece suite became a trampoline, as I leapt over the first chair, landed on the settee and bounced straight into a huge puddle containing the second chair. I thought about sitting down for a breather to take in the landscape. The chair with its large, protruding springs resembled the Slumberland version of an Indian bed of nails. Delivery trucks passed by, one completely drenching me from head to toe. With dirt water dripping down my nose, I caught a glimpse of the cheering driver as he drove off. He seemed to be saying, 'got yer! Yer little bastard!' What he didn't know was I'd enjoyed the drench as much as he had. Suppose those pot-bellied, motorway-sweethearts have got to have fun somewhere.

Against a pub wall I noticed an old inflated bike tyre. Lifting it above my head, I threw it down the road hard as I could. As it bounced, I bounced straight after it, yelping inside with the pain the rubber had caused by pulling my hair on its downward spiral. A car full of young lads pulled over offering an unwanted lift. Drawing close, I noticed laughing faces, back seat. Window down, 'Town Called Malice' playing and finger beckoning, I knew what was coming next. They roared away, skidding in the process.

Set free, I felt I had to wash all traces of the job away from my body; an impossible task, as small steel particles and Old Johnno's cigarette smoke permeated every pore of my clothing. Boy, was I in a hurry to lose the shitty office togs!

Leaving the shackles of nine to five behind, my imagination did the twist. First I pretended the cranes dotted about the docks were old Johnno's soldiers trying to drag me back to the warehouse. They looked like huge, steel dinosaurs coming up over the dockyard wall. I could see jagged splinters inside the holes of derelict boats as they floated alongside other strange and unusual looking vessels of the sea. A gap in the huge dock wall presented me with a jigsaw picture of twenty or so coloured Popeye tugs, with no skinny Olive Oil aboard to brighten things up. Bobbing up and down, all different in colour, they were sadly surrounded and shaded by grey. The bigger ships in dry dock, rusted beyond repair, got me thinking, *bit like the whole dock-industry around here,*...I slowed down to encapsulate the whole scene.

Cut-throat Thatcher and her heartless Pirates had stolen all the jobs away, down to the south coast. Me, I'd just thrown mine away before she could. The old place didn't lift me like it used to, I needed to dream. I was young, this place was old. *New York, New York, it's a wonderful town.* Ah, not to worry; it was a shit job anyway. The Pirates of privatization had sailed to power a few years before, and anybody who didn't fancy sailing in the bad ship Thatcher was going to have to get used to hearing the words, *'It's not economically viable. Close it down – throw them overboard!'* Soaked through, it felt and looked like I'd been thrown overboard. I'd learned some valuable lessons about keeping my head above water, but it was getting harder and harder to swim against the tide in this City. The water seemed to be constantly flowing south.

Carrying on down the dock my imagination kept twisting away. *I wonder what would happen if I kept walking...say, to an airport, or train station? Would I lack the courage to jump to a new destination with no baggage in tow? Or, simply bottle-out and trod those well worn kitchen tiles back to the apron strings, to face the music and Daddios shiny size nines?*

Trying my luck away from home before I'd landed on my feet quite easily. Locally, jobs were scarcer by the week, as most headlines told of one company closure after another. After making a big effort to land the Trainee Managers position at the steel stockholders, I didn't think I'd be going down that road again. You know the one: Please, please, please, give me the job sir. Bit like Yozzer Hughes in 'Boy's from the Blackstuff'. 'Giz a job, go on, giz a job', I can still see that big, porno-star mustache, the dark overcoat, the pleading face. 'Go on mate, I can do that.' I suppose some people can beg, and get used to begging, and some people can't and won't. It takes a certain type of desperateness to reach that point. Me, I'd become absolutely determined I'd rather die than reach the Yozzer stage of proceedings. Thinking about the book I'd been reading, got me thinking some more. *Get out of my fucken way, I'm Jack Kerouac, I'm free, I'm on the road.*

Town approached. Sponge-like and drenched to the bone, I stopped at a level crossing and felt a ghostly wind blow right through me. For a moment I thought it might be my Docker grandad trying to push me back in the other direction; wanting me to go back to work and be a steady Edward like he was. All I crave is freedom, fresh-air, a decent menswear department and a whole new rig-out. Move away granddad, you've had your day, this is my 1980s. Senses hyper, mind playing overtime, skin tingling and wrinkling at the same time, I strode on. Murky water dripped into my eyes, drenching every orifice. Jumping into an empty phone box, to dodge the granddad-wind, reminded me to phone Paddy. Unbelievably, the graffiti artists hadn't reached its door...the piss artists had though. His Ma answered. The wind whistled through the hinge gap, making her sound like she was speaking from Anchorage, Alaska.

'Hiya Mickey love. You've just missed our Patrick. He left a few minutes ago in a taxi to Lime Street Station.'

'Why's that Mrs. McArdle?'

'He said he was gonna visit Boney down in London. I think he finally got fed up waiting for Tommy or one of his other uncles to phone, you know, with a job start in that Jacobs biscuit factory.'

'Join the Club,' I interjected; the pun going over her head.

'Any idea what train he was gonna catch Mrs. Mac?'

'Yeah, the one that goes out of Lime Street.'

'No…I mean what time? Ah forget it Mrs. Mac, its ok. I'll see you later.'

'Ok Mickey, tara love.'

Looking upward to check the time on the huge Liver bird clock, I thought of how it sounded when Paddy's Ma said Boney instead of Anthony – funny how nicknames never sound the same when parents use them. I smirked when I thought of the job mad Tommy would have lined up for Paddy regarding the Jacob's biscuit factory; then wondered how Tommy got his inside info on when the wages got delivered? It was 3:15 in the afternoon and Paddy had just left home. I knew the London train left at five past the hour. If I sorted myself a tasty, new rig-out in the next 40 to 50 minutes, we might be lucky.

Peeping from behind the phone box door, the Liver buildings dwarfed me. Walking quick-step, I made my way up the Water Street hill that led away from the Pierhead waterfront. Finding shelter from the wind, whipping up the Mersey estuary from the Irish Sea, was priority. Since I'd stopped running body sweat had quickly turned cold. My stinging nipples were about to fire bullets.

Meanwhile, my coat and other garments, heavily drenched, drew me toward a Laurel and Hardy walk. My finger ends had badly shriveled, like Dracula had used each one as a drinking straw. With senses on pure overload, I likened my appearance to one of those January 1st head-cases, the ones partial to dressing up New Years day, before diving headlong into an ice laden sea or freezing cold lake. The tipped-over-the-edge part of my imagination went further, likening the feeling to that of an Egyptian Mummy: on the brink, not yet dead, but uncomfortably wrapped in ice cold bandages. Difference being, I was wildly alive with a desperate need to peel the bastards off.

'Warm clothes, where are you? Warm clothes, where are you?'

Shivering along, I started with a daft mantra to get me over the next two hundred yards or so. I stood at Castle Street near Liverpool Town Hall, the business district, the office blocks part of town; not the place to find new jeans and trainees. Basement and street level takeaways jostled for sandwich trade, while small menswear outlets, dotted here and there, sold formal wear to the tie and collar brigade. It's not what I'm after. What you might call the 'Suits you Sir' part of town. Seven foot dummies dressed in office attire stared down at me as though I was a poor, daft tramp and they were the wise-arse 007's, inside in the warmth, looking suave and sophisticated.

With hyper-senses and shivers kicking in again, the mantra started up. 'Warm clothes, where are you, warm clothes, where are you?'

An old lady threw me a pitiful look. She weighed me up as though she was thinking, *looks a bit young for a tramp; ah, poor boy, maybe he's a homeless beggar?* While I'm thinking, *No love, don't open your handbag.* The purse came out. *I'm off before she asks to take me home for a good scrub and a nice warm bath. Come on, where's all the decent clobber shops?* I know where they are, but I'm impatient. Killing to get rid of the soggy work reminders, you'd have to lobster pinch to find an air gap in my glued-on second skin. Half-drizzle, half-sweat dripped from nose to chin. The nose drops tasted like they'd come straight from the Mersey. The chin drops made no impression on my saturated chest. As they sank away, I'm thinking, *bit like the job prospects, eh.*

Relieved at reaching the entrance to George Henry's, a half-decent department store, I noticed front door security eyeing me up and down. Right away I know he's got notions I'm another impoverished welfare wonder, tiptoeing along the social breadline, trying to go unnoticed while out for the day on the rob. He clocked me in that oh-so-obvious way. Like the old lady, he stared too long for my liking. It got me thinking about a verbal assault. Nah! If I were him looking at me, I'd have a good, long look too. Squelching into the posh carpet swiftly brought an assistant over.

'Hiya mate! Can I help you with anything?'

A good start; I liked his friendly manner. First impressions told me the Dennis Healey eyebrows could do with a trim. Caterpillar man came close. My god, if the Bizzies raided a Stones backstage party Keith Richards could stash a bag of skag in those eyebrows! Or, they could double up as an expensive set of mohair mudguards on a designer racing bike – minor details, minor details – join the real world you daft nugget! I answered his friendly manner in a friendly way. 'Listen mate, I'm usually okay to pick some gear out. Give me five minutes and I'll give you a shout.'

'Sure, no problemo; give us a nod. By the way, I'm Dennis if you need any help.'

'Ok Dennis, cheers mate.'

Dennis with the eyebrows eh, I'm thinking…I'm off again with the details. *Shall I ask him if his second names Healey; ha ha! Nah! Boring; probably gets that one every day in this place.* Stop thinking, start doing.

Grabbing clobber by the handful, to get to the changing rooms double-quick, doesn't help Robocop's imagination. Sauntering over for a gander, gets me thinking some more. *I've heard of giving you the once-over, but this feller's gone head to toe, toe to head, head to bleeding toe and it's getting embarrassing.* He's like one of those nodding dogs on the back shelf of the car in front: up, down, up, down. With fuse burning and brain seeking utterance, lips shifted gear. 'Listen mate, why don't you take a hike. If you get any closer I'll let you keep me oul undies – Ya weirdo!'

Seeming to get the message, he gave a parting glance that said *I've heard it all before*. Then, in mock-army manner, he marched his big Sergeant Major boots back to the realms of door duty. What a Pinball Wizard! With the light dazzling from those blinding toe-caps, if sunny, and that beaut had you down in a fight, you had no chance of dodging the kicks he'd bounce off your fucked-up barnet!

Entering the changing rooms I noticed the pop-star posters stuck on the back wall of each cubicle. Duran Duran – shite! Spandau Ballet – worse! Culture Club – for Christ sake! Can changing room decor get any cheesier? ...Spoke too soon. It can. It's Soft Cell! Marc Almond, the Fairy Muppet of electronic pop stared down at me, as if to say, 'Show us you're package trucker'.

Only two left. Yesss...Kate Bush wearing a white leotard; looks the one for me. Checking the last cubicle for luck...Ooh! Close one this, Kim Wilde telling me to come on in. Kim's another darling. Let me see; Kate or Kim, Kim or Kate? The voice of reason interrupted: *Details, details, get in and get changed Dickhead!* Kate's raspberries won the day, jutting beautifully through the tight, white leotard. Her face: that girly, English rose look, with everything below a woman in full-bloom, meant Kate had become my three bar electric fire. Tingling skin embraced warmth. With imagination in over-drive, the thought of slowly peeling off my sweaty garments till I'm arsehole naked in front of Kate was all the central heating my bollock region needed. A knock-on-effect slowly gave body temperature and brain a long awaited boost. *If the desired warming effect carried on this way it might bring that naughty but nice feel to things. Off with the rags.* Looking above leotard level, into her eyes, I'm thinking, *Hi Kate darling, I know I've looked sharper but, it's been a rough day'.* The mind was doing the twist again. You could say, yeah, the warped mind would.

Pulling the changing room curtain across gave me the chance to finally get rid of my saturated work togs. Coat and shirt – straight over the head – mint-rocks and shoes – kicked aside – kecks and undies – mere rags, peeled off in one. Naked, I had a little peep to see if any eyebrows or boots were in the vicinity? Then, using the changing room curtain, I dried every crevice that squeaked or reeked. *Excuse me Kate darling, a stream of cold sweat is running down the crack of my arse. Needs must!*

Wrapping it around my head like a woman getting out of the bath, it did some good; stopping cold water from dripping down the nape of my neck. Next, it became a baby's nappy. Naturally, like Paul Simon said, I started *'slip sliding away'.* After the armpits, the bellybutton and the Rubik cubes, I sat on a chair inside the cubicle, lifted my feet into the makeshift bath towel and neatly wrapped them turban-style. If the dim-looking Robocop marched in and clocked the feet, he'd think the welfare wonder had changed religion from Orthodox Church of the Holy Handout to some new dyslexic Moslem faith.

'You okay Chief?' Falling off the chair, legs half-tangled in the curtain, thoughts interrupted came crashing in, in the sound of Dennis' voice.

'Fucksake! Err…Yeah, Yeah its Ok Dennis, I'll be out in a mo.'

Rising, I untangled myself from the curtain, the chair and loose clothing strewn about the cubicle. The curtain had pulled completely off the rail so, taking another peek outside the changing rooms to see if Dennis' mudguards still hovered, I began sweeping old and new garments into one large bundle. Good, the good server wasn't in view; time to move. Nipping three cubicles away, I dragged whatever I could down the corridor. Being Tuesday afternoon, with only a naked lone shopper jiggling his bits around the changing room, it was obvious who'd wrecked the Kate cubicle, but, I mean, some things you just don't want to explain.

About to throw my sweaty, mint rocks at Simon Le Blob for trying to look the wild boy, I stopped. I'd done enough damage. The weight of those socks could've banged a hole in the flimsy studded wall or, needlessly drawn attention. It was tempting though, you couldn't miss that clam-of-a-nose. Looking at the poster of the eye-lined, Duran Duran singer, I thought his face bore a strong resemblance to a burst basketball, or maybe the brother of Miss Piggy...*Oh well! No more three bar fire. Not a hope of any heat emanating in the walnut department there then.*

Throwing the stinking work clothes to one side, I tried the new stuff. Suffering with sweaty arse syndrome: a sandpaper case of the old dreaded ring-sting, I moved like the off-road cyclist who'd been to Aberdeen and back. Zipping back to my in-store bath towel, I rubbed so hard between the San Fernando Valley I almost started a forest fire. Between toes also needed a decent pipe clean before I could apply some fresh socks. Cold and wrinkled toes made me think of leftover crinkle-cut chips...no sweet salt and vinegar aroma though.

Buttoning up the brushed-cotton, Ralph Lauren Polo shirt felt like pulling on new skin. I luxuriated in the warmth and feeling of the fresh garment. A pair of 32 inch Levi's fitted snugly enough, except button-up jeans would be a bit draughty without boxer shorts. Those steel buttons were a pain in the cakehole when you were out on a drinking bender. It wasn't time to be choosy. Bottom line – get me – I didn't fancy shopping around for a different pair. No way could I have put any of that sweaty work gear back on before leaving George Henry's. Apart from the heavy, wet condition, it looked symbolic lying there in a stinking, squelching heap. Damp and smelly, it reminded me of old Johnno and that shitty, rat infested warehouse. I wanted to push that thought as far back up the Dock road as possible. Good thoughts only now, at least till I go home...hmmm...if I go home? Come on George Henry's, do me proud. I need a full rig-out...now!

Pulling a lamb's wool crewneck over the shirt instantly did for me what Simon Le Blob could never do: it brought good feeling and warmth. Though medium build, foraging for loose and comfortable was always a timeless choice on the rig-out agenda. Never one of those Norman Wisdom type fits. Ease of movement: essential.

'Dennis, where are you mate?'

I called a little louder. 'Dennis …Hello, Dennis!'

His head appeared at the bottom of the changing room corridor. Standing outside, being a polite shop assistant, he craned his neck around the partition wall; unlike some of those Freddie Mercury type shop assistants, who'd waltz straight in whistling '*Bohemian Rhapsody*'. Not being homophobic, just needing to know the difference between the stare of a Floorwalker and the gaze of a cock clocker. You could only see Dennis' head, giving his cashmere caterpillar's even more prominence; sort of Zebidee from the Magic Roundabout; bit trippy dippy.

'You rang m'lady.'

I'd been wrong about Dennis Healey and the Magic Roundabout; he'd turned into Parker from Thunderbirds. Lady Penelope's servant quietly answered my call.

'Dennis at your service; you found what you want matey?'

'Yeah, just some socks and shoes Dennis, please.'

Following him to the footwear department, I noticed a pair of Timberland shoes and asked for an eight. Dennis took a minute or so to reappear with a shoebox and a pack of cotton socks. 'What about your other clothing? D'yer want me to bag it?'

'Not yet Dennis, I might leave it here. Let's sort these shoes out first.'

Walking about the shoe department told me the shoes were too tight.

'Nah Dennis, toes are squashed. Let's try an eight an' a half; see what they feel like.'

Dennis took his brows for a browse in the stock room, while I checked for Robocop and his mirror-toed Sergeant Major boots. He was off clocking another customer who didn't look quite right, someone who didn't match up to his man at C&A photo-fit. First impressions meant everything in his line of work…mine too.

Scanning the shop floor for plain-clothes Floorwalkers, cameras or other mirror-toed Robocops came back negative on all counts. Negative meant affirmative. Toward the side exit I noticed a large antique Grandfather clock chiming away at 3:45; time to join the wide awake club.

Dennis Healey, Parker and Zebidee all rolled into one arrived back on the scene carrying two shoeboxes. The man had a fine bounce in his stride. I liked Dennis. He spoke mid-approach. 'Right matey, let's see how these go. Timberland leather can be quite hard to begin with. It really only becomes supple after a few weeks of wear. In my experience, like most well made footwear, you'll only feel the true comfort of these shoes after they've been worn in.'

Slipping the shoes on, tying the leather laces, I strode up and down. Over by the hat counter I glimpsed Robocop chatting away to a nubile shop assistant. Hair tied up, tweedy but tasty, she seemed to be enjoying the gleam in his eye as much as he enjoyed the gleam in his boots. He was well involved. Not a sign of any floorwalkers or cameras.

'Listen Dennis, to be sure on size, can you get me a nine?'

'Sure matey, with the amount of money these cost they've got to be just right.'

As he walked into the storeroom, I thought for a second, *There's no money coming across today Dennis,* and walked straight out the side door.

Catching sight of big boots, number 10-15 down the law enforcement job ladder, I was tempted to walk faster but, it was laughing time. He was still too busy trying to tell an impressionable young girl about how he would one day stomp his way around the world with the British Army. Somebody needed to tell Mr. Top-polish he'd never climb the security ladder in those shiny, Pinball Wizard's. His big, bad, boots were the last thing I viewed. Two polished Hackney Cabs on the end of your legs. What a beaut!

Out past St. Johns shopping Precinct, round the corner

past Blacklers department store and there was Lime Street Station in all her glory, beckoning me in. *Come on in Mickey son, there's trains in here to all parts of the Kingdom.* Having a final look towards George Henry's told me security had parked his taxis, meaning green light stories. Mingling with the crowd inside the bustling railway station told me it was vanishing act complete.

US AND THEM

1st Class, 2cnd Class, Toilet Class

First steps into the Station were slow, I wanted fast, as I navigated my way through hordes of excited school kids with their teacher chaperones. The afternoon sun had finally broken through, as sunrays bounced off a throng of radiant little heads. Raising a hand as a sun shield, to guide my way through, I noticed the lady teachers failing miserably at getting the kids to line up underneath the big, old, Lime Street clock. Busy looking for the departure timetable, I collided with a little redheaded kid carrying a lolly-ice. It flew from his hand on impact. Other kids looked at me like I was the Kiddie Catcher from Chitty Chitty Bang Bang. Putting them at ease, I pulled a Mr. Happy face, and thoughtfully enquired of the youngster. 'You alright mate?'

'Piss off Knobhead!' Came the eager reply, as he tried to catch his sliding lolly-ice. I half-laughed in surprise. He must have been seven or eight with seven or eight thousand freckles. Joking, I threatened, 'Ay, I'll tell your teacher on you!'

To which he finished me off with, 'Hurry up Shithead, she's over there!'

Innocence, innocence, where art thou innocence. *I suppose he won't suffer fools,* I thought, as I found the departure board.

The London train left in 5–6 minutes from platform 8. Marching straight onto the platform, hoping to find Paddy, I found him four carriages up sitting comfortably reading a newspaper. He hadn't seen me through the window. Stepping furtively through the carriage door behind him, I shouted, 'tickets please!'

Giving a severe jolt, he banged his knee in the process, setting the two of us off.

'What the fff…! What are you doing here?'

It was useless trying to talk; giggles had boarded the train. Laughing long and hard, some passengers smiled at us, while others looked out of the window in mild embarrassment. One elderly lady, a lovely, shiny aura about her, so bright and glowing she looked angelic, commented how refreshing it was to see young people so happy and cheerful on meeting each other. 'What a lovely way to greet your friend. Gosh young man, you're appearance has even cheered me up!'

'Cheers love!'

Glancing at angel features, I made a note to watch my language in front of her. With cheekbones shinier than Robocop's toecaps, the lady glowed. She looked in her sixties. Normally I'd avoid contact with people of her generation, as during my brief working life I'd been constantly hearing the doctrine of the 'We can all be Millionaires Party', and I'd become seriously disillusioned with wrinkly, high profile politicians telling me I too could climb the ladder of financial success like they had, when the only ladder knocking about where I lived, belonged to either our dopey window cleaner or my Ma's old tights!

You'd hear the bastards rattling on about profitability, economic meltdown and growth fucking industries – all from the comfort of their swanky Chesterfield settees. It stunk of Mr. Opulence from Surrey, telling Mr. Shit-on from the North, to get off his fat lazy arse and he too could one day drive a Range Rover round the Home Counties. Nah…couldn't see the rungs on that ladder myself. Deeply mistrustful of most senior people since the O' Level age, apart from family or local people who'd been through the same kind of job-there there job-gone treadmill as myself, the older people on TV and in newspapers were all down as money-mad, power tripping bullshitters! It seemed they had their own fake ideology going on, their own set of phoney standards; a do as I say not as I do type set up. Anybody young, sit in the corner, be quiet while we fiddle the books. Bit like old Johnno and the South Africans thinking about it. And, I'd come up against other old Johnno's, old Whitey's and old Tories before. The Sid James fella I'd left on the Dock Road wasn't the only bullshitter amid this 'Carry on chatting shit' movie set.

Relaxed in our seats, I explained to Paddy about work and my shopping escapades, while he told me about his Uncle Tommy's recent court appearances which had become a 'headline trial'. The clouds opened up again. As the train sped down the damp track its rhythmic rumble rocked me into drift-off. I had to get my head straight about the last few hours and what a London venture might lead to. In possession of a meagre wedge and no belongings didn't bother me, my only problem was how I would phrase the eventual phone call back home. I'll leave that till later; didn't need to put family on a bigger downer than they were already on.

When doubts start to flow in one half of the brain, sing a powerful song in the other. *'I am a one in ten; a number on a list, I am a one in ten, even though I don't exist. Nobody knows it, but I'm always there, a statistical reminder of a world that doesn't care.'* The UB40 boys were back in town, and me, back among the dole-ites. I knew the words well. Paddy's probably thinking we're going down the Smoke to see Boney for a few days, few laughs, few drinks; then we'll trot back up north for another slow-walk on the sign-on treadmill. Like I knew the words to the song, I knew this sabbatical was going to take longer. I'd let him know my plans later.

Paddy wouldn't scoff at ideas I had cooking. One thing I didn't need on that journey was a reality check. Reality was starting to look a bit grim. That afternoon I'd rejoined the sign-on crowd – the de-waged – which would've no doubt hit me like a fucking sledgehammer when I walked through the front door of our humble drum. Me Ma and Da would've been okay after the initial shock, it's just it would've been hard for them to digest on impact, seeing as most of our family were already ditched, drop-kicked and dole-queued! It seemed half the street and, most of the young people I'd been brought up with, were either unemployed or scratching a living or, had given up and pissed off to sunnier salaried climes.

A lot of unemployed kids, devil again finds work for idle hands palaver, started testing drugs like some people test out yoga, or the gym, you know, to see if it works for them. Some Dole-heads-became-Smack-heads-became-Crack-heads, to eventually plug in stolen hi-fi's at their own shitty, little squats, before slow dancing around the barren room to Neil Diamonds, 'Love on the Rocks'. Jokes aside, I knew I'd reached the end with unemployment, formal interviews and the Yozzer 'please, please, gimme a job' routine.

Other side of the pauper's pickle, some of that same dole queue had started selling their souls when they noticed the lucrative profits to be made from serving-up the heavier users, and, in so doing, thought they could fast track their way to the Range Rover lifestyles of their Tory contemporaries. All of those budding little Jeffrey Archers starting to blossom in 1980s Liverpool dole queues – funny one that!

Drift-off came to a jolt when the train screeched to a halt at Stafford; time to join the wide awake club. The Clippy would be on his way soon and neither of us had any tickets to ride…as per usual.

'Paddy, come on lad, its Stafford. Toilets, luggage or walk-past?'

With three ways to bunk the London Train, I was thinking

on my feet. *Walk-past involved waiting for the guard to walk to the back of the train after Stafford junction. Bye bye to Stafford, he'd walk forward clipping tickets. Once past the buffet carriage, situated between 1st and 2nd class, you'd zip past him. If he tugged you, you'd tell him your ticket was back in your coat. Once he'd clipped beyond your seat, you could return to where you'd been sitting. If he still pulled you, to ask if he could see your fresh-air-pass, you'd tell him he'd already clipped it further back. This worked 90% of the time; the other 10% meant straight to the bogs, or between the seats where they left a space for luggage. Lodging in the luggage space, you'd sit where a suitcase sat; placing a coat or bag over your legs and feet, thus becoming luggage. The toilet trick involved locking the door and sitting tight until the Clippy passed. They started to unravel this obvious ruse, by knocking and waiting outside the door. Realizing this, we'd leave the door ajar. Unless you were Shamu the whale, or some other Big-Mac-character, you'd stand behind the unlocked door to let Mr. Clippy think the toilet was empty. There was enough room to stand comfortably, even if he pushed the door open. Proceeding on to the next carriage, you'd appear and, hey presto! 'Where's the sausage rolls Paddy?*

The walk-past being the most effective bunking technique, meant the luggage and toilet escapades only occurred when the train guard was Indian or Pakistani. Always vigilant implementing a stowaway search, as though proud to do their duty for British Rail, the Asian Clippy's were masters at playing 'Keep British Rail tidy' and 'Hunt the Bunker'. It was make your mind up time, which depended on the Clippy of the day. *Though I had a couple of hundred quid severance pay, that was about to abandon my pockets faster than any good-looks Paul Daniels had a chance of acquiring after puberty, once we reached the Big Place. British, old Johnno train guards, fed up listening to excuses from people like me – who could blame them – had an attitude and mannerism that said, 'Don't give me or the passengers a hard time for the two and a half hour journey, and I won't change into Sergeant Choo Choo, the British Rail Top Cop.'* Minor details, minor details.

'Paddy, wake up lad, its Stafford.'

The train eased its way down the platform; the signal for ol' snip-the-ticket to appear. Leaving Stafford, he walked through bellowing his usual instruction. 'Could you have your tickets ready for inspection please?'

Without turning I knew ol' snip-the-ticket wasn't on duty. Today, Mr. Eager Mohammed was clipping, and, to a man, Asif Clippy's were strictly British Rail rule book. Time to get on your toes I suppose. The lengths and detail I went into just to bunk the train showed how skint I started out, while also showing my early attention to minor details so everything ran smoothly.

Paddy, waking properly, rubbed his eyes mid-yawn. 'Uh Uh! It's Asif.'

'I know, you can tell the voice a mile-off.'

Though we didn't give a flying fuck about politically correct zealot opinion, calling Asian Clippy's Asif's wasn't a racist gesture. The nametag came about a few months earlier when we'd paid Boney a weekend visit. Given valid for three months, used, but unclipped tickets, we presented them to the Asian Clippy. He seemed unsure of the validity – correctly so. Before taking them to his little room at the top of the train, he turned and said, 'Asif the tickets are Ok' in a heavy Asian accent. Asif was how it sounded to us. The name stuck.

Passing to the rear of the train, he'd soon clip his way up. On reaching the sliding-door to our carriage, we'd be off for a brief sojourn to the toilets. Asking angel features if she'd like a cup of tea, she looked jammed in her seat.

'Ooh that would be nice. Milk and two sugars please. Here, let me get my purse.'

'No it's Ok love; I'll be back in a mo.'

She looked puzzled as to why two fit, young lads had to visit the buffet. Paddy turned to the lady. 'Must stretch the oul' legs ay.'

She quickly replied, 'Ooh…wish I could; I think I'm jammed in this chair.'

Thoughts precisely, I'm thinking. I smiled back and drifted into one of those weird deja-vu moments where a sequence transpires and you're going, *definitely happened somewhere before,* and you know what's coming next.

The lady spoke. 'You two lads look like men on a mission?'

Paddy answered. 'No, not really; we're only going to see our mate Bone…err Anthony, he's been staying in London for a few months.'

'Can I detect a little concern in your voice? Is he not the brightest star your friend Anthony; if you don't mind me saying, that is?'

'Say that again love; he's a right soft-shh…Err, yeah, he's a bit dim at times, yeah.'

Watching Paddy being careful with his P's and Q's, I'm thinking about her intuition. He was doing a fine job at passing the time of day, while the old girl seemed to be genuinely interested in the two of us. As the conversation takes place, I'm stood taking it all in, mouth half-open, unable to speak, knowing exactly what's coming next. *Weird,* what's that medical reason the experts always give: one part of the brain picking up signals slightly ahead of the other? Well, that part of the brain knew this was the bit where we scarpered, as the young Clippy reached our carriage – keen looking fella too.

'Paddy, come on, the tea'll be getting cold.'

Catching drift, he told the lady 'Be back in a mo love.'

One of the two toilets was locked. We entered the vacant one. Minutes later we listened to Asif edging past our seats in the adjoining carriage. 'Tickets please; next stop will be Watford Junction. This train will be terminating at London Euston.'

'Paddy, stifle the laughter.' I whispered, as he stood on the bog seat trying to give me leg room; doing monkey impressions same time. The familiar hissing noise of the sliding-door opening and closing told us he was outside. Departing footsteps marched up the train to the next carriage. Stooping to look through the bent bars of the door ventilation grill, I got a tremendous view of Asif's white socks and half-mast British Rail pants. His rail strides had ridden so far up his legs you could see the red and blue stripe at the top of his tatty, white tennis socks. *What a smoothie! Got to be the Bryan Ferry of the railways!* Indicating the coast was clear, I turned to Paddy. 'Sausage roll sir? Go back to the seats; I'm on buffet duty today.'

'Right you are sir.'

Leaving the cubicle, I'm clocking the spy hole, thinking, *who the fuck damages these door ventilation grills? Fellow bunkers looking out for Clippy, or sweaty-pervs looking in to catch a blimp of female bush?*

Passing Asif, I gave him a nudge to register eye contact, so he wouldn't need to see a ticket on return. His clear, brown eyes glinted. He looked young to be a guard: sturdy and upright, hair like Elvis. Sort of British Rail, Bollywood sex symbol in the making, till you clocked the half-mast pants and tennis socks. At the buffet, loading up with tea, scones, napkins, a couple of cold drinks and anything else at hand, meant I'd struggle to produce a ticket if he stopped me on the way back. Hopefully, young Asian Elvis would read things my way. Viewing the other travellers, I thought how relaxed they looked, not having to duck and dive like me and Paddy. I gave Asif a nod and a half-glance. He gave me green light, making space to pass through. Reaching the seats, I passed the drinks. 'There you go love.'

Radiating kindness, she thanked me profusely. The lady's look and manner seemed unworldly. Staring, I wondered if she applied Mr. Sheen to those cheekbones. Catching me mid-stare, I offered her a scone in mild embarrassment. She refused, saying she was on a diet. *Diet!* The word snapped me back to the rattling carriage. *Diet! Come on love. Live for the* moment. *It's wooden overcoat in a couple of years; means sweet FA when your belly pushes the lid up.* I felt guilty thinking of the old lady in such a cold hearted way.

Thoughts interrupted showed in the shape of a suited and booted, twenty-five stone misery guts, who plopped most of his weight into my lap as he waddled through the train. With the majority of his bulk pinning me to the seat, I reckoned he was a heavyweight conscience saver. The Burtons version of Les Dawson didn't smile when Paddy and I sniggered as he dropped his two bags of train nosh. Noticing the big ship Miserable Mouth sailing aboard three chins, I made no attempt to gather up the nosebag about the seats. Struggling to bend and retrieve his tuna sarnies, I got a full-whiff of the worst B.O. snorted in Britain since Giant Haystacks was bed ridden for a week with mad wrestler's flu. Without a hint of an apology, he lifted the blubber welded around my frame and took his pants full of lard for a further waddle towards double seat comfort. Angel features gave a loud tut. 'Poor manners some people.'

It was drift-off, time for train ride dreams. I loved the train. Concentrating on passing scenery the noisy engine mechanism became soothing background noise. Hopefully, any problems I'd had at boarding might seem trivial and unimportant at destination. London would undoubtedly present me with a whole new ball game than the one I'd just blown the whistle on. Let's go. Yeah, with the Rattler, drift-off came easy. With barely one eye open, I scanned the lush English countryside with everything painted in shades of green; my art gallery in motion. The train weaved its way through Villages, Towns and Cities, before entering black tunnels that led out to farms dotted with raggedy-arse sombrero wearing scarecrows, or just plain old mop-handled, crucifixes topped with baggy hats.

Arriving at Watford Junction the changes in landscape became less rustic: more building brick and tower block.

Nearer to London, grey concrete and steel choked the last remaining green fields as the claustrophobia of urbanization set in. Compared to ten miles back the colour of a small, grassy park became so enhanced that, like the saying goes, it seemed to leap out at you. North London tenements and ugly council flats umbrella'd the railway track to such an extent, that I wondered why they didn't cave in with the rumble of a hundred angry trains nagging at their footings every day. Paddy's voice came from afar. 'Look at these flats next to the tracks. What a shitty place to live!'

Stirring, I said, 'You know what they say; I'd rather have a caravan in the hills, than a Mansion in the slums.'

He looked toward the passing tower blocks, nodding in agreement. Euston approached, cue Paddy's piss-poor Cockney accent. Trying to be the Pearly King, he sounded more like an Australian fruit farmer chewing a bag of plums. Normally a decent impersonator, with London lingo he was lip-ripped and uncoordinated. The train edged its way to the gate. The last couple of shunts brought us to a juddering stop. Pulling his bag from the luggage rack, Paddy smiled, 'Boney boy's gonna be in for a shock when he sees us two, Mickey!'

It dawned how lightly I'd travelled. Watching others struggle with luggage, I thought how many could have gotten away with bare essentials: toothbrush, money, a pair of heels. Was it personality or shoplifting that allowed a no baggage motto? The ability to pick up necessities as you went along, or the need to feel un-burdened? You couldn't count on Boney for necessities like soap, toothpaste, a hairbrush; the lad was a hygiene law unto himself. I'd take care of that later. In his skull, London was paved with sovereigns and, in his own cartoon wisdom he thought all Southerners were soft-shites born into money. Once those same southern soft-shites fully evolved, they walked around places like Carnaby and Bond Street with bundles of the stuff falling out of their back pockets. Laughable – tell me about it!

The sharks in the capital, fighting for bigger spoils, had more snappy tiddler's to contend with; with a greater chance of being bitten or ripped-off. Not that Boney had anything to rip-off, but you could be sure that the first few bob he earned a Bookie or some other shark would be waiting near the banks of the Thames to separate him from his dough. Liverpool in comparison was a lot more parochial. Walk ten miles in any direction and you'd be out of reach from the sharks operating within its boundaries. The accent was a dead giveaway. Ten miles out and the speech pattern went all Milltown: boots, braces, mining communities; people of good sheep shearing stock. London's boundaries and accents were not as clear cut or defined, and tended to peter-out after 20, 30, god knows how many miles. It was definitely Britain's metropolis. Try explaining this, by introducing a little colour into Boneys black and white world was wasted logic, and would only leave you disillusioned about the human race and its basic function for storing general knowledge. People like him were never going to find a bag of Sovereigns lying about.

The night before he'd phoned Paddy telling him to get his arse down there prompt. He was picking up 50 Quid a day, cash in hand! He'd ended the call telling Paddy that, 'the Geordie site agent was a sound fella; as solid as the Tyne Bridge. Give Mickey a shout, we'll have a ball,' his parting shot. Before replacing the receiver, Paddy, knowing how Boney gets his facts messed-up, asks, 'How d'yer know the site agent feller's a Geordie anyway?'

'The lads on site said he's from Middlesbrough.'

Paddy, realizing his error, goes, 'Nah, they're not Geordies, you call them Teesiders.'

Boney countered. 'No, you've got it wrong Paddy, he doesn't live by the beach.'

Paddy didn't bother explaining and ended the call. 'Forget it. I'll see yer tomorrow.'

Boney's sound and my sound were Blackpool to Las Vegas

apart. The last time in London I'd given him some terrible stick, when he'd invited two supposedly *sound* fellers back to his even smaller ex-bedsit, to kip the night. They ended up being a couple of student speed-freaks from Brummieland who talked double-Dutch till the crack of dawn and found farting under the covers amusing. Still having a nark in my knickers over the Walsall wanker who'd robbed me and my brother in Frankfurt, meant the two nailed-on Midland knobheads were serious candidates for getting the blame. You know how it is when someone from a certain place does you wrong and you end up hating the whole town, city…or fucking country for that matter. You know it's born of ignorance but you can't help let it colour your view. Those two fools at Boney's didn't realize that each time I heard that accent I thought about the Elton John lookalike spending our Deutschmarks on rent boys back in Germany, and felt like volleying them all the way back to Spaghetti Junction.

In our haste to leave the confines of the train we'd forgotten to say goodbye to Angel features. Looking back, she struggled with her bags. Nudging back through the carriage, I lifted them from her grasp out to the passageway, purposely whacking a few people who stood and watched her struggle. She gave me a big kiss. 'Now don't forget Mickey, you're the wiser one, you look after those other two?'

She's supernatural this one, I'm thinking. Her words got stamped in my memory box like the First Commandment. Walking away, I couldn't get over how she glowed, like everyone else on the platform seemed insignificant. Looking at Paddy, I wished she hadn't said the last bit.

Boney stood waiting at the top of the platform slope, a rolled-up Racing Post in his hand. The football hooligans' weapon of convenience they called a Millwall brick, was Anthony's magic wand; so he thought! His gambling habit developed when a long stint on the dole left him with enough time on his hands to either play with the rolling-pin between his legs all day, or start walking to the local Betting Office to push his meagre pittance through the cashiers bars for a giddy-up ride on the gee-gees. Like all bank-on gamblers, he'd have his moments, but in keeping with all true gambling fiends, he'd have to sink his oh-so moderate winnings into chasing after that illusive big win; the so called, *boss tip*, the *dead cert!* Boney studying the form, fitness and riders of the day's horses was ludicrous, like an idiot pretending he had inside knowledge his friend's weren't attuned to. Reality being, they were thinking, *what a fucking golf ball!*

Paddy, first up the platform slope, accordingly greeted the white Aborigine in his Australian farmers' accent. Boney hadn't caught sight of me in the rush of passengers exiting the station. He looked along the platform like a 95 year-old granny with Fairy liquid in her eyes. For the fun of it, I walked up to him and almost glared into his face – not a glimmer – and straight on past. Giving Paddy the finger to the lips, I walked to the middle of Euston Station and stood watching the two of them.

The clock above the departures board read seven o'clock. People streamed all over the station concourse on their way home from work. Some carried shopping bags from daytrips to the West end, while others embraced like long lost friends returning from, or departing to, some far off Northern city. Early evening sun shot neon beams of light to all parts of the station. Taking in the scene, my two buddies, thickly outlined in white, stood out profoundly from the passing throng. Funny, it was another Kodak moment. I felt an affinity and a bond I've never felt for a friend or friends to this day.

Paddy smiled. I waved at Boney, trying to get him to focus. I began dancing; evolving into Chubby Checker doing the Twist. About to break into an all-black, Maori war dance, Paddy, giving up, pointed his woolly skull in my direction. His blurry eyes zoomed in. I imagined him older, whacking a white stick through numerous shop doorways, till eventually finding the one you opened to find cigarette smoke filling the air and a

TV bellowing the names of the day's non-runners. The old fella next to me, thinking I was a station scrounger trying to earn a crust, turned to me. 'You should be on Top Of the Pops son.'

I replied, 'Yeah, that's why I'm down here today, you know, for the auditions an' that; just getting a last bit of practice in.'

He added, 'I had a feeling you were a real dancer. I could tell.'

Me? Dance? He must be blind as Boney. The man seemed pleasant enough. I told him I danced like an office nerd at a Chrimbo party. Realising I was no scrounger and just a happy camper, he laughed and reached out to shake my hand. 'Good one son!'

As Boney approached we were shaking hands and laughing.

'Hello Mickey, what the fu…err…wharra you doing here?'

He stuck out a hand toward the ol' fella. 'Sorry, what's your name?'

Surprised, the man shook Boney's outstretched hand. An introduction was in order. I interrupted, 'Anthony, this is me Grandad.'

'Oh right, hello Mister…err? Hang on a minute I thought your Grandad was dead?'

The laughter erupted again, and intensified when the man said, 'fancy saying I was dead like that!'

Conversation over, I looked at him. He'd put me at ease. For an instant he hadn't seemed old at all, sort of childlike, bubbly and happy-go-lucky. With a dab of his infectious, ebullient nature he'd given my spirit an instant lift. I silently wished there were more like him. Wishing bon voyage to a second pleasant pensioner of the day told me they weren't all cynical killjoys like old misery guts from the steel warehouse. Prototype whacked, I'd be doing voluntary work for Help the Aged if this carried on.

Exiting toward Euston Square tube station we noticed a commotion near the mainline doorway. Sauntering over, I noticed Willie Whitelaw the Old Tory Lord bustling his way through. Thinking, *one chance only*, I pushed through to the periphery surrounding old pug-dog features. Up close, I spotted he was flanked by tough looking bodyguards. Getting them to drop guard, I delved into a true-blue Tory impression. 'Lord Whitelaw, Lord Whitelaw!'

It didn't get me any closer, or get pug-dogs attention, though his musclemen eased stance. With a new technique needed, I chose the long, lost nephew approach – the family recognition type voice. 'Willie, Willie, it's me Peter!'

He looked like he'd been continually smacked in the gob with a frying pan for sixty-five years, a bit like the brother of FBI boss, J. Edgar Hoover – another pancake face. He looked me over. One more was needed, more familiar, more uppity, only louder! Willer, Willer, It's me, its Peetar!'

A small gap opened. The bodyguards relaxed their carpet-carrying stance a little more. Lord Whitelaw, looking directly into my eyes, tried to recognize me. I helped him. 'Willer, Willer, It's me Peetar!'

With eyes locked on mine, I lowered the posh accent. He stared, using one of those 'Oh, I realize who you are now faces', like when somebody greets you using your name and you haven't the faintest who you're speaking to. So as not to appear rude, you pretend to recognize them, by either faking or giving a really slow greeting, making time to fathom out the person's identity. It looked like I was Mr. Whitelaw's lone detractor, as Pancake face went through that old recognition rigmarole on my behalf. My voice and vocabulary changed dramatically, 'You dirty, fat, stinking, Tory twat!'

The words rolled from my tongue like I'd practiced them for weeks. Thing is, I'd spat with such venom, I now struggled to find any spit at all. Managing to dredge some up from somewhere, I let fly, landing most of it on one of his assistants walking closely behind. The ensuing bedlam had me ducking amid his smarmy on lookers. Everyone within his inner-circle started swinging for me. Hair-pulls, followed by slaps and punches, landed on the back of my head as I fought my way out of the scrum. In the melee, I caught sight of Paddy and Boney looking confused, then caught sight of Willie's carpet carriers fast approaching. Paddy reacted quickly. 'Aye Aye, he's only a kid, take it easy will yer!'

Ignoring the plea for clemency they marched forward. Grasping at straws, I pointed behind their Tory boss. 'What about the two with the sticks?'

Momentarily, they turned to look. In the half-second it took…Bang! The starting gun went off. The moment of skedaddle I'd been edging for was there. *Out of the way, man running for his life.* Out the right hand exit, up Euston Street, then left onto North Gower Rd without looking back, I'd run a World record for that well trodden path. Stopping at the top of the Underground stair rail there wasn't a soul to be seen. Resting my hands on the rail, I took in huge gulps of air. Scanning the street in preparation for the next part of the race came back all clear

A large Pakistani family appeared from the bowels of the tube station. Filling my lungs, they eyed me warily, while I wondered why the men's shirts were hanging out. A child at the back of the group threw me a huge, cinematic smile. I gave him the thumbs up. He reciprocated, giving me another big grin. What a smile! His chops lit the street. The kids smooth chocolate skin wildly exaggerated his white teeth; earmarking a special place in my employment chain breaking day. Strange the way someone or something can scribe a place in your memory box from a fleeting glimpse, while other more frequent routines and everyday people leave no trace at all.

Outside the kids' smile I noted two huge posters advertising Simply Red and Sigue Sigue Sputnik records. With those two woeful pop groups alongside Pug dog and his men in black, it got me thinking, *Fucksake, had Punk music and its ideals achieved nothing?'* It wasn't ten years on and things had already turned all Pete Townsend on us: '*Meet the new boss, same arrogant, pancake face as the old boss*'. Whitelaw reminding me of FBI founder, J. Edgar Hoover, got me thinking some more; *had Hoover and Whitelaw both been quarried, shaped and educated at FBI headquarters – The Flat Boat-race Institution.*

Paddy and Boney walked up the Euston Road looking like a pair of *Johnny-go-homes*. Paddy shouted, but the boom of London traffic stopped me hearing his voice. He came close. 'It's laughing, they never left the Station. Those muscle-bound, carpet carriers might be alright at headlocks, but they've gorra catch you first.'

Boney looked me up and down. 'Fucksake Mickey! You're not in London five minutes and you're causing murder.'

I tried explaining why I'd acted up and that, given half the chance, Lord Whitelaw would have been on the receiving end of a lot more than spit and bad language. Before finishing, Boney butted in. 'Alright Mickey, I know who the fat bastard is now; you coming to work tomorrow or what?'

Scolding myself for explaining things, Paddy interrupted Boney, asking did he know the quickest way to Illford where he lived.

'Err…we just jump the Circle line.'

'Don't we change at Liverpool Street?' I enquired.

Paddy, reading a tube map, ended the guessing game. 'To get to Illford we have to catch an over-ground train from a mainline station. If we wanna go by tube, first we get the Circle-line to Liverpool Street, then the Central line to Gants Hill. It's a good walk down that Cranbrook Road, the way we went last time.'

'Come on Boney lad, wakey wakey! Paddy's only been here a couple of times and he's already showing you the way home.'

'He can show me all the way to the fucken door if he wants! I can't be arsed with them tube maps anyway.'

Paddy looked him up and down. 'Then how the fuck are you gonna find your way round London, Dickhead?'

'Ay, I've gorra good sense of direction these days; I'm getting to know the streets of London quite well.'

'Shut the fuck up Ralph McTell, here's the train.' I informed him, laughing as we boarded the tube. The laughter continued in the silent carriage. People nearby looked annoyed. Tell you, I never had a clue about invading somebody's body space till I'd been in London a while.

Changing at Liverpool Street, we jumped the Central line to Gants Hill. After a good stroll we arrived at Boney's pad. The street, full of large, non-descript detached houses, was middle Britain to a tee. Boney told us a stack of them were owned by some Scotch gangster landlord, instantly nicknamed Hamish McRent. An apt moniker once we realized how greedy the stingy, money-grabbing bastard really was. Any room with decent floor space he'd partitioned with studded walls. Each night you could hear the fella next door breathing, never mind the TV, music or night time nooky. Each bedsit cost forty quid a week, and with each house containing roughly ten bedsits, this Hamish McRent guy was one seriously minted Jock.

5

GET YOUR FILTHY HANDS OFF MY DESERT

The moment Boney opened the front door I searched for the bathroom. Desperate for a shower, I was suffering badly with the ol' dreaded ring-sting. After rubbing too hard with the changing room curtain between Crack Valley, a fire now slow burned in Blood Orange Gulch. Treading gingerly upstairs, we entered Boney's bedsit. Facing the street, same houses and a street lamp being the view, two beds and a spare sleeping bag were the arrangement. A small, portable TV, mounted on wall brackets near the window, pointed down at the room. Apart from a huge poster of Pink Floyd above Boney's bed, some strewn garments of clothing plus a couple of NME music magazines, there was nothing else of note.

The poor lad had been living in an Illford jail cell, with cheap Heinz Beans air-freshener cloaking the surroundings. I opened the window. Beneath the other bed lay a pile of nudie books. Judging by the cup and saucer stains, it looked like the stack of flesh mag's doubled as a pull-out bedside table. I asked why he'd left them on show. He said he loved the fact he didn't have to stash them away beneath the carpet underlay, like he did back home. His strictly church going Ma and Da would've had a religious fit if they found his hidden wank-bank. Eyeing a beaming Hugh Hefner aboard the top cover, I wondered how Mr. Wide-Mouth would feel if he had to spend a little time inside Boney's Playboy mansion.

Hosed-down, we walked to Illford's small town center and hit the lager. Promises were made about not getting tanked-up, with the building site beckoning the next day. Coming from a city full of big time drinkers I'd seen what the demon drink could do to people and, weekend binge apart, I'd remained vigilant that I'd never get sucked into any permanently poisoned lifestyle. Noticing a callbox near Illford Palais night-club, I told the other two I'd follow them to the next boozer after letting family know why I hadn't returned for tea.

Getting straight through, and to the point, explaining what had gone on at the steel stockholders, it would be a big under-statement to say they were not pleased. But, I suppose it's hard to convey condemnation messages to a son who's just upped sticks and left home without notice. I was made-up when the phone call ended with them telling me to take care of myself and not to worry about facing any misery music. My Da surprised me before he put the receiver down when he said, 'I can understand you getting upset over false promises made by bosses and Politicians. I've been listening to their Bullshit for 30 years. Who knows, maybe your generations not going to listen anymore? You take-care kid! Soon as you're fed-up or pissed-off down there, always know your beds waiting upstairs in this house.'

It was a pick-me-up-and-a-half, but, I wasn't daft. I knew any return home – once the initial honeymoon period had worn off – would eventually end in grief. A few weeks after being velcro'd horizontally to the settee, like thousands of other Autograph Artists back home, it would be an altogether different voice I'd be hearing. The initial family reunion talk would be followed by a pair of size nine Doctor Martins connecting fiercely with my back Levi pockets, sending me sprawling off the big, comfy couch and straight out the front door to catch the first train leaving Liverpool to London all over again.

Those *'it's your own fault'* statements, emanating from the honeymoon-over-voice, would've been like squirting water pistols full of Alsatian piss into each lughole once they kicked-off. I'd reached the stage where I had no intention of returning home. Not until I'd at least found. A: a job. B: a few-quid, and C: I could walk through the front door with a smile as wide as Dawn Frenchs' knicker elastic or, half as wide as that Pakistani kid's outside Euston Square.

Walking back to bedsit land a drop of rain got me thinking how the building site might be full of mud and, as I'd only got the one outfit? *Fuck-it, I'll worry about that tomorrow.* Back at Non Descript Street, a half-drunken penalty shoot out was organised at the gates where Boney lived. Walking back we'd found an old case ball, quickly christened, Thatcher's head. After kicking Thatcher's head all the way back to the rusty gate, a penalty competition got under starters. Top two pen-takers would earn themselves a mattress for the night, while the worst would have to doss down on the itchy floor. Being Boney's flat, he reckoned he was going to sleep wherever he liked. Paddy began arguing with him, till he realized I was steering clear of any disagreement. He looked at me steering clear. 'How come you're saying fuck-all?'

'Listen Paddy, it was only a few hours ago I saw that pile of smut mags next to his bed; if you wanna fight for the right to lie in his crusty bits, so be it.'

Boney was immediately installed as England's new no.1… well, he had the same *bag of frog's* hairdo as Peter Shilton but, that was about it as Thatcher's head flew past him on every occasion. At sudden death, a miss by Jimmy Dean and it looked like it was all over. The star studded penalty bash ended when Steve McQueen stepped-up and hammered the final penalty through the crap goalies legs; winning himself the use of a crusty, jail cell mattress for a hopeful night's kip. Meantime, Jimmy Dean's bad miss ensured he would have to be the rebel without a bed for the next eight hours.

The moment the light went out and head touched pillow, the old doubts set in about packing in the job. Zebidee coils jabbing away at my spine meant I was instantly missing the big, comfy flock back home. My mouth, meanwhile, had turned into a Lancashire cabbage farm. Having no basic belongings began to irk. A toothbrush, a change of clothing and a new working day would hopefully change things, with gaining work remaining priority. Its availability began to trouble me more than anything else. Whether there was a start on site stabbed at my brain throughout the night. Boney had reassured us that Bernie, the site agent, would have us grafting our bollocks off by 8.30 sharp. I prayed it wasn't another empty Boney utterance. I didn't need to be knocking around with time on my hands, or worse, to be fucked around by another building site blagger.

Early dawn, the sun shone through a small gap in the curtains. From half-five onwards it bounced of my forehead like a laser from Captain Kirk's gun. Every way I turned or tried to hide the beam followed. The handkerchief size curtain's had no chance of dousing the light. A little before seven o'clock, after a restless night of tossing and turning, I sprang from the bed and announced in a loud, snooty voice. 'Rise and shine darlings; time to greet the new day and put your best foot forward!'

Paddy yawned. 'About time too, I've been awake for ages!'

I kept with upper-crust tones. 'Why didn't you wake me old bean, could've done a spot of night fishing.'

Boneys scraggy head popped over the covers. 'What the fuck are you two on about?'

Tipping his mattress up, we left him squashed against the wall with his feet sticking up in the air. Underneath, you could hear him moaning. 'You're not funny you know. I've got to tidy this fucken' room. If the jock gangster knows three people have kipped here, I'll be out on me arse, you pair of divvies!' It's my flat yer know, moan, moan, moan...

Paddy and I could still hear him bitching as we battled for the downstairs bathroom. After a dishcloth wash and a wrestle over Boney's three bristled toothbrush, we eventually left the house to walk up Cranbrook Road, past the park, to join the other commuters at Gants Hill tube station. We had to travel west to Liverpool Street mainline station where the site was situated, and, where Boney led us to believe a hundred other sites were up and running. True to his word, construction was everywhere. Building site fervour hit me flush on the chin. If Liverpool and the North were being squeezed into decline, the South was being nourished and overloaded with economic nosebag.

The site he worked at was just around the corner from the station, in an area called Bishopgate. Totally alien to me, little did I know, soon I'd be stomping around this part of the Eastern Central Line, and the few square miles surrounding this part of the London Underground, as frequently and as often as any of the briefcase carrying, pinstriped power-broker's that swarmed the area like ants. Entering the main gate I became aware of a large notice nailed to the entrance frame. It stated in messy, hand painted letters: 'HANDYMAN WANTED'. Underneath, it said, 'Good rates of pay today'.

Muttering brief greetings to his fellow workers, Boney led us to a little hut at the side of the site. 'Bernie! Alright mate, these're me two mates, Mickey and Paddy, will they be okay to start today?'

'Err...It should be alright, if they can graft. You two Scousers then?

'Yeah, yeh!

'Let me make a quick call to okay things with the main man. Hang fire lads.'

He dialed using a connected landline, with wiring pinned around the walls of the wooden hut. As he spoke, I'm nudging Paddy, whispering, 'Look, a Geordie Sergeant Bilko,'

Boney squinted at me angrily. A lookalike always described somebody quickly and effectively. Though, if it was a dead ringer, laughter always followed. Bernie Bilko was a ringer alright. The glass in his Eric Morcambe national health rims looked pub ashtray, triple-glazed. My immediate thoughts were that he wore similar glasses to Whitey in Jo'burg, and that I wouldn't fancy holding a nail for him to knock in! With Paddy set to burst, and me badly wanting a job, I stopped clowning about. A minute later, Bilko put the phone down. 'Yeah, start no probs. Any specific trades lads?

You couldn't tell who he was speaking to. I broke the ice. 'Alright Bernie mate, I'm Mickey, I wouldn't mind having a bash at that Handyman's job stuck on the gate.'

Giving me the once-over, he asked, 'Ok Mickey, let's see… Can you lay brick?'

'Err…No not really.'

'Ok. Never mind, can you do a bit of joinery?"

'Err…no I can't do much of that.'

'Ok then….Can you do a bit of plastering?'

'Well…not really to tell yer the truth.'

'For fucksake man, how can you call yourself a Handy-man?'

'Well, yer know, I only live round the corner.'

After a second or two everyone laughed, except Boney, who sat there stone faced. Thank god the tickled included Bilko. He piped up. 'Serious though fellers, if you have any basic skills let us know. Other than that, it'll be the same as your mate Anthony.'

Boney had spoken about day to day labouring duties during last night's beverage. He'd been working the site for the last six weeks. Apart from some heavy lifting, he reckoned the graft was a doddle. I'd been on a couple of building sites before and the hod-carrying I'd done was no fucking doddle! I'd also been a Scaffolder's labourer for a short time in Aussie and that job gave you muscles in your foreskin. We'd see about Boney's doddle. Before we began, Paddy, building site virgin, asked, 'Any boots and ovees Bernie?'

'Ovees? What the fucks ovees? You Scouser's have got names and abbreviations for everything…Ah! Wait a minute. I know what you mean. You mean overalls don't you?'

'Yeah, yeah that's right', Paddy chirped.

'Well, you'll get fuck all like that here mate! There's a wagon coming through the gates any minute, start unloading that. Ok fellers.'

First thoughts were that my new clobber was about to get wrecked. Till second thoughts took over: *Fuck the gladrags! You need the dough more than clean clothes!* Paddy, wearing nattier threads than me, and not too keen on mucky hands, started looking skyward like he was contemplating walking back, out of the gate. True, I felt like doing an about-turn myself, but knew I had to stop running and start earning someday. Someday, was right now! Noticing the awkwardness of the moment, I cheerfully offered, 'Listen, I'll tell yer what, let's have a giggle all day. I mean, we'll do the work an' that, but let's keep a smile going, alright! No miserable kippers allowed on site; agreed?'

Paddy nodded. He knew the dance. It was time for graft and a bit of self-discipline. Though we'd just arrived in town, I wasn't looking for any bedding in period. If Bilko wanted three good Labourers, then we were the boys. We had never worked together in a 9-5 capacity. Whenever we'd met up before it would be for a bit of skullduggery, or we'd be socializing and weaving in and out of boozers in town on a bender. The closest we'd been to producing toil together was lifting the odd settee onto a bonfire every November the 5th. Hearing me speak, Boney scratched his head and crotch piece at the same time. 'We can't start arsing about you know. If we're laughing all the time, they'll think were fucken' about and show us the door.'

'Listen Boney lad, have you ever heard of the seven dwarfs?'

'Course I have.'

'Then whistle while you work, *toodle do do do do do.*'

Sounds daft? Well, it's the way London working life began. I spent the whole first day in good spirits by acting like one of the seven dwarfs at a whistling contest. It soon doubled as a mantra, for repressing negative thoughts like doing a runner back to home comforts. When negativity came strong I'd whistle a rendition; sort of mind-control the simpleton way. It worked so well first day, I let it continue the next, and the next, and before you can say 'where's Sleepy and Grumpy', the only thing missing for this hard working dwarf was the lovely Snow White, who never seemed to be waiting at Hamish McRents at the end of the labouring day. Oh for a night of country comfort at the little cottage in the woods, instead of another night spent shacked-up at an Illford bedsit with two hairy-arsed, Liverpool ball-scratchers!

Early site days, I caught a few workers eyeing me in a peculiar way. I didn't speak much the first few days, preferring to get my head down and concentrate on the task at hand. A couple of them caught me staring blankly into space, mid-whistle. Sometimes the whistle kept me awake mid-afternoon, after another sleepless night spent staring at a lone, swinging light bulb, with loose Zebidee springs jabbing away at my back. After living like Illford's answer to the '*Young Ones*', with a bit more anarchy and a lot less room, and a few weeks listening to Boney farting and snoring, I was ready to blow first week's wages on one night in the Dorchester. Watching a white, male Aborigine rise and shine each morning was only funny for a day or two. The head and ball scratching routine soon wore off as a morning sideshow. With Thatcher's head lodged firmly between the aerial and the chimney, the evening's penalty competition had been terminated for good. We tried sleeping head to toe, but the bed was about as wide as a hot dog bun, and once your onions fell into the middle, the other persons fell out of the side.

Three settee cushions, taken from outside a furniture shop, became the third bed. Once sleeping conditions slightly improved, amid shoebox conditions, we had a nifty grafting routine on the go. Getting up and out to work was never a problem, as we were all desperate to get some real fresh air each morning. Jumping out of bed early, to leave for work on time, became a pleasure. I grew more determined by the day about not returning home with biscuit crumb pockets, or with no upwardly-mobile-dreams shimmering on the horizon. Past experiences had taught me that life was not fair, and that the sooner you grew a set of testicles with the size and bounce-ability of two World Cup case-balls, the easier you'd get on and get by.

Apart from the odd game of football on Cranbrook Park, evenings after work consisted mainly of tube bunking as we went sightseeing all over London. Noticing how a lot of the shops stayed open all-hours, especially in the tourist areas of Piccadilly Circus, Charing Cross and Covent Garden, the Hoister's apprenticeship continued. Whenever we missed family or home, listening to the foreign accents of migrant workers – not tourists – hard at work, made us realize that two hundred miles up north was around the corner compared to where these people had come from. We'd repeat, 'Who the hell are we to moan? Look at these poor bastards from all corners. At least we're only a two and a half-hour train journey away.'

We spoke to a host of homeless Northern runaways of a similar age to ourselves. Unlike them, kipping under West End lights, the Daily Express, or a stray Coppers hoof was a Jupiter distance away from my agenda. Early evening forays into London's bright lights, allied to late shops, meant pilfering with light fingered Larry soon showed face. Nothing serious at first: clothing, records, tapes, groceries that type of stuff; along with a few restaurant runners – every week. We started visiting Garfunkel's buffet restaurants, where after stuffing ourselves with enough nosebag to feed twenty homeless runaways in one go, we'd have to do a walk out, never mind a runner. Garfunkel's were raking it in, every night of the week. To stroll out after gorging was never a problem.

Working most Saturday's, we hit the ale every Friday, Saturday and Sunday. Saturday morning in work was spent trying to skive; usually battling for a cushy number like sweeping the yard. Still signing-on, dole money paid the rent. The bedsit it paid for started getting seriously cramped, due to growth in personal belongings: designer jackets, shoes, even socks. Everything else: records, more clothes, toiletries, bath and bed linen, we lobbed into the pad. Soon we were struggling to stand up, never mind lie down. The odd bit of pilfering became a light-fingered London fixture within weeks.

We were getting paid fifty quid a day on site, but didn't see any money till Friday afternoon when Bernie Bilko handed the wage packets over. Due to past experience, I wasn't too keen on this set-up. First week, we got paid at the end of each working day. Then, we started getting our money like all the legitimate, cards-in employees. Main difference: our wage packets didn't have pay slips inside, as in, 'cash in hand', which was rife in 1980's London. I wasn't comfortable with the thought of some site agent going off 'Florida Phil style' with our wages. If our 'paying man' got the urge to do a hometown runner one lonesome Friday night, I didn't want to be the paying man paying for it. It had happened before with the Walsall Wanker, and what was to say Bilko never had a loan-shark debt as big as a Mandelson mortgage up in sunny Middlesboro!

With this in mind, I opened a Barclay's savings account at a Liverpool Street branch. I told the others to do likewise. They ignored my financial advice. Though none of us noticed the immediate significance in this, they both told me on numerous occasions it was the one mistake they regretted big-time. I suppose I had more to lose by going home, having not yet climbed the foothill base of Moneybag Mountain. I'd shown good intuition in school, passing O' levels and CSE's quite easily – when I bothered to turn up. The other two, just hadn't turned up.

Acquiring a steely determination to succeed at something, I knew I had to put a few bob aside while things were beginning to look vertical. Meantime, Boney was flinging his hard earned wedge full-tilt into the first bookies on the road; either that, or it was tucked inside the first tart's knicker elastic he came across while taking a sex stroll down in Soho. From Friday night to Monday morning Paddy was living like he was taking part in that Brewster's Million's movie, you know the usual: Weekend you spend it, Monday you lend it. Then it'd be birds, booze, booze and birds, followed by more spend it and lend it. Then he'd be like a fucking paraffin lamp for the remaining five days. Clothes-wise he'd be dressed to a tee, but he wouldn't have a fluff-ridden Jaffa cake in his skyrocket!

Par for the course, Boney caught his first dose of VD from some scragbox down in one of those seedy Soho dungeons. He booked himself into the clinic for a brief examination of his scabby rolling pin. Confirming he'd picked up Knob Throb, the nurse told him he'd have to return for his medication and check-up every Tuesday for the next few weeks. Typical Boney, he told us catching a dose was a blessing in disguise, seeing as next door to the clinic was a betting office. Always look on the bright side of life!

Paddy started tagging along with his first steady London lady, whom he'd copped-for Saturday night at the Illford Palais. He was also meeting a gorgeous, young office temp he'd blagged on the morning tube for some lip-munching lunch. He looked dead funny meeting her in his scruffy building togs, with her all dolled-up and looking heaven-sent. On site he was getting called Illford's answer to Warren Beatty, due to him having two or three ladies on his main menu. It's the reason I was happy with the leftovers. A few London lovelies got wise to him acting the Warren and, once they'd cottoned-on to his shenanigans, and come blabbing to me, I'd to give it the 'Yeah, he's a right Bastard that Paddy fella,' simply to get a bunk-up. Fact of life: most young fellers will do or say anything for the sake of a bit of nookie.

Some nights, finishing graft, one of us would say 'Who fancies going over to that Madame Tussaud's?' And that's how evening jaunts to the bright lights began. One night at the London Planetarium we went to see a light show with music from Pink Floyd's *Dark Side of the Moon*. Taking in the show, Paddy noticed this bird in the back row eagerly playing her fellers flute. We weren't staring heavy or anything, it's just they were so obvious and carefree. Before you could shout, '*light show nosh*', the fella starts beckoning us over and we're thinking about it, but laughing our plums off at the same time. So Boney goes, 'She might be one of those she-devils who bite's your cock off?'

I added, 'She'd have to be Jaws the Shark to bite your knob off Boney. Anyway, look, there's camera's in here. I wouldn't wanna be in some security guard's porno flick.'

Paddy, the shy one, says, 'Fuck you'ze two, I'm going over for a coppers cosh.'

With that, he strolls straight over, drops his kecks and undies and before Roger Waters has a chance to play the next guitar solo, she's pulling him round the backseats of London Planetarium while '*Money, get back, I'm alright Jack, keep your hands off my stack*' bounces of the cinematic walls. The lights swung around, catching his hairy white arse every ten seconds. Every time they did, Boney and I keeled in bulk. Boney said, 'Ok Mickey, we having some or what?'

'Fucksake Boney, your coming out of your shell aren't yer; looks like Soho's finest have deffo straightened you out!'

He carried on laughing, while I'm thinking, *if I don't go over now, there's no way I'm going after Lenny the Lash. Once the Queen of the Laser Beam puts her lips around Anthony's Swiss Roll her mouths gonna to end up like a burst bike tyre!* Paddy strolled back towards his original seat, fastening his jeans.

Soon as he sat down, he took a look at me. 'Never happen back home Mickey.'

Whereas the lightshow nympho had pulled Paddy around the seats, she seemed only too happy to oblige Boney with a little bit of her trumpet playing technique. Again, as the lights swung round, you could see her singing into his microphone. For the briefest, it was as though she was singing directly under the spotlight, making her the first Karaoke singer we'd ever seen. I didn't saunter over to the Laser Beam Queen. Not comfortable performing in front of mates, me with a girl was strictly doors locked, no viewing, pure one on one. Strange really, when you think a lot of the time I'd only be with a girl in the first place because of Paddy's philandering ways.

London life was bringing Boney out of his shell alright. You could see him growing in confidence around strangers. He was still half a scarecrow when it came to everyday living though. Like one Saturday afternoon at McRents Chicken Coops, when he left the communal bath taps running to almost flood the house. Deciding he'd like a sandwich with a soak, he started the bath before going down to the kitchen to make a quick snack. Realizing there was no bread or milk he forgot about the taps and shot out to the local Seven Eleven…

Half an hour later we heard a knock at the bedsit door. It was Brett, a local pot dealer from Canning Town. He said while doing his dope deliveries, he'd knocked at the front door to serve-up Clifford, a six foot six Rastafarian from Jamaica who lived across the landing from Boney. When Clifford answered the call to let him in, the two of them noticed water dripping from different parts of the ceiling. Being almost as dopey as Boney, they'd come knocking at our door, as, in their eyes, we were the resident Liverpool builders. Walking into the bathroom I simply turned the taps off. I knew instantly it was scatter-brain, after he'd told Paddy he was going down the hall for a bath. When I knew he wasn't inside the house…It didn't take A' level Tenancy.

Boney eventually walked in, knows immediately what he's done and starts to explain. Once he got to the bread and milk bit, I interrupted, 'Well, where's the bread and milk soft-shite?'

He started to walk out the door, saying 'Bastard! I've left the bread and milk in the Betting Office!'

'Oh, neglected to tell us about yer little diversion didn't yer…Willie fucken' Carson!'

We spent hours and hours trying to dry ceilings that showed damp or water damage. I even brought plaster back from the site to fill some minor holes that appeared the day after the flood. Lucky all the tenants hated Hamish McRent, otherwise the Jock mingebag might have been told he had two fellers living rent-free in one of his Chicken Coops for the past couple of months, leading to baseball bats at six paces. Boney was always *'just shooting down the Betty'*. Like most full-on gamblers it zapped all of his dough and most of his free time.

Apart from Clifford the lanky Rasta, the other tenants included another black guy called Barry. We didn't get to know his second name as he was always first to the mail, being based nearest the front door. Being a twenty stone, pork chop, it's why we called him Barry White. We never borrowed any of his pants for lifting expeditions, though. The three other rooms on the ground floor where occupied by three Scottish lads, busy trying to be the new synthesizer kings. They were all Human League, white socks and pass the make-up lads; wearing those daft, cardboard collared, Hitler raincoats, topped with loads of eyeliner and mascara. At first we thought they were a bunch of homosexual Midge Ure's, playing synth music twenty-four-seven…sorry, twenty four hours a day, hardly ever coming out into daylight. Once we got to know them they were decent lads and often sauntered over the park for a game of football.

Soon as we knew it was going to be one of those lovely, balmy, sunny evenings, the ones you get in England, late spring, early summer, we'd want a game. Ten minutes in, with sweat making mascara run – looking like a group of weepy, girlfriends returning from a tearjerker at the fleapit – we'd be in stitches. Returning from work when it was going to be one of those fresh-air nights meant staying in the bedsit was like choosing to sit in a sauna with Brussels sprouts as coals. Giving the Raincoat Jocks a knock sometimes wouldn't suffice and you'd have to scream to be heard over the wailing drones of synth-pop. 'John, Gavin, Davy, come on, it's dead sunny outside! England versus Scotland! You up for it or what?'

One of them would eventually poke his nose around the door, as though you had to make the decision that they were allowed out. At first, slow recognition of other life. Then, once it clicked they could freely join the outside world, they'd come legging out like a group of hostages been trapped in a Bank safe for a week. Dedicated keyboard kids the Jocks. Crossing the road to Cranbrook Park, goals were set up at pre-named ends. Ours, naturally, the Wembley End, with John, Gavin and Davy's, the Hampden End, meant game on. Booting the ball into the air the Raincoat Jocks dribbled toward the Wembley End, still wearing those glued-on Hitler macs. Gluing fingers to keyboards and raincoats to skin ultimately paid off, when two of them appeared on Top of the Pops a few years later.

The remaining tenants were up on the second floor, in rooms adjacent to Boney's Chicken Coop. Terry Spencer, who slept in the coffin next door, came from Salford, Manchester, so we'd have the Scouse/Manc banter going on. Terry, a young Elvis Costello, loved his music and loved using his arse to try and knock down the flimsy studded wall between his and Boney's room. Trying to demolish the dividing wall between the rooms with Bernadette, his girl who visited from Oxford, got us referring to her as Bernie the Bolt, seeing as Terry was always trying to tighten her to the floor or wall. For the same reason, we called Terry the Salford Spanner…

Whenever Bernadette paid a visit we'd utter, 'The Berlin Walls coming down.' I met her in the communal kitchen a few times. She looked like butter wouldn't melt; as a lot of academically inclined types do. She reminded me of a sixties Cilla Black, in glasses, with those same Bugs Bunny front teeth and that bouffant hairdo. This Bernadette though, got up to a lorra lorra shagging! Terry visited the Ilford Palais with us, knew everything about music and told us he wanted to be a music journalist. Sometimes I'd catch him in the morning going to sign on, before he'd go off to writing courses in college under an assumed name. 'Fucksake Spanner, how you gonna get your certificates if you're using an alias?'

'Loads of writers use an alias Mickey. I'll just have to stay with mine.'

Ha! Come to think of it, maybe it's why I've never seen his real name in the Melody Maker, NME or Q, or any other music magazines. One night, playing football with the keyboard Jocks, I noticed him walking through the park with Bernie the Bolt. Kicking the ball back to us, I whispered to him, 'Ay Terry, play them Bunnymen and Smiths albums a bit louder tonight will yer?'

'Ah! Finally getting in to some decent sounds, ay Mickey?'

'No, it's not that Spanner, it's so we don't have to listen to you and Bernie doing your DIY knock through all night?'

Walking back to Bernie, he laughed out loud. I could hear her going, 'What did he say? What are you laughing at?'

The last tenant upstairs was Miserable Tits; named because she was a full-on man-hating lesbian. On the odd occasions you'd bump into her, she'd give you a look like you were dog shit stuck in between the ridges of her Dr. Martens soles. She wore denim jackets, denim jeans, denim shirts, probably denim knickers, and a denim pussy with a small orange Levi tag for a clit. She looked like Dopey Dolph Lundgren, the beefed-up, blonde action man from Sweden. She had short, blonde, spiky hair and was built in the American fridge-freezer tradition. Overall body, I'd say Dolph, yeah, but the facial features didn't carry over too well. Whereas the blonde action man was a bit of a Greek god in the looks department, her face resembled a week-old peach thrown against a wall. She wore those huge Lesbian earrings that said 'Woman to Woman' and 'Men can get to Fuck'!

Sharing a fridge with the other tenants, I lifted three huge trifles from Sainsbury's one day and placed them on the top shelf for an evening treat. Coming home early from work, sneaking in, I found her dipping her fingers into one. She tried to act nonchalant, dipping her fat fingers again, like it was hers. I thought of an old Pink Floyd track and tried to make a joke. 'Hey, get your filthy hands off my desert!'

She looked at me like I was mad, put the trifle down on the table and walked off upstairs without turning back. In all the time I lived at Boney's Chicken Coop I didn't see Face-ache smile once and, the only conversation verging on normal I had with her after that, took place outside the bathroom one Sunday morning after I'd just had a wash. She asked me. 'I hope you've left the toilet and bath as you yourself would like to find them?'

Trying to break the ice, being friendlier, so I thought, I said. 'You'll have to hurry up, by the time you've taken all that denim off there'll be no hot water left.'

'Ignorant bloody man!' She bellowed, adding, 'It's probably you who's been leaving dirty, great stains of piss all over the seat!'

'Don't think so love. I make sure every last drop goes down the plughole in the sink!' Surprised by her guttural tone and offhand manner, I'd gone for winding her up.

'A filthy man with a filthy tongue…who comes from a filthy place!'

'And what's so filthy about where I come from cake robber?' I enquired.

'I've travelled to Ireland before…the place is fucking putrid!'

'Ireland? Ireland? What the fuck are you on about? Listen

love, talking about filth and stink, I went into that bathroom after you the other day, and I can honestly say that for the first five minutes I was in there I thought somebody had left a dead rat behind the sink! You've been eating too many trifles.'

End of conversation. With the exception of Miserable Tits, the other tenants got along just fine. Socializing, we'd sometimes watch TV in each other's rooms, and when that year's World Cup tournament kicked-off we decided we'd take turns in shooting out to the local 7–11 for food and ale before any big games. It was always me, Boney or Paddy who brought the goodies back, as the rest of the Chicken Coop community were concrete crust and mouldy green cheese merchants. Noticing them living day to day, we'd often comment. 'Fucksake, they make us look rich!'

The odd game of footy, watching footy, games of cards, listening to music and tourist expeditions around London was how we spent the spring and summer of 1986 in bedsit land. Evening jaunts around the City stemmed from a need to get out of our confines, and from being ex-Northern school kids where teachers went on and on about all the history, important buildings and monuments down in the capital. Through teaching they'd gained a sort of mythical status. Being able to travel about London with ease, we made it our duty to view most of them. Like everything, the viewing novelty soon wore off, while the lifting habit entered Smack-head proportions. As the weeks passed, I decided to make a weekend visit back home. Asking Paddy and Boney if they fancied a change of scenery, they agreed, Friday, pay day, was the ideal time to head back to Liverpool.

As it got nearer, I looked forward to a couple of nights on the ale back home; praying that nights of intoxication would end in serious backdated shut-eye. Each night I climbed into that dreaded hot-dog-bun-of-a-mattress, I'd close my eyes and try imagining a soothing nap in the big, comfy bed back at Mother and Father Bears on the banks of the Mersey. But, each time someone farted, or bedspring jabbed at cheekbone, my imagination hit recall, and the realization I was slap bang in the middle of Stalag Chicken Coop acted like a toffee hammer to the head. Life progress wasn't supposed to include pointy bedsprings, foghorn snores and dreaded brown smoke.

Checking progress, I began comparing where I came from to this pound-sign, rat-race, and wondered if me getting a 'proper job' with 'potential' would only lead me directly to more years of having to pander to southern versions of old Johnno. Every day at work I witnessed thousands of them dressed in dark suits, to-ing and fro-ing from Liverpool St. Station like an endless stream of soldier ants; marching out of the exit holes of Liverpool Street underground in their droves. Here, they got to grips with their individual jobs of work, before returning home eight hours later via the same route and same hole in London's pavement. Whereas ants returned to the hole with something sweet and sticky in tow, the suits, neutered by compliance, were out gathering as much money as possible before returning to their own waiting queens at some three bedroom, red-bricked semi in Curtain Peep City.

It may have been a flawed, simplistic, youngish view of things, and, it's only when you're older you realize everything is much more complicated and multi faceted but, it's still very near the truth. Once you're older, jaded, more cynical and worse for wear, after beating that same money path year after year, means nothing ever gets viewed as simply again. Shame really.

The ceaseless droves of office workers were often the butt of building site mirth. Being engrossed with money-marching into work on time usually meant any quip floated straight over their pre-occupied heads. Certain suits within the Yuppiefied throng we'd give self-explanatory names: The Bandy Fucker; Billy Silver Wig and Tatty Briefcase. Others, like The Pinstriped Yeti, needed explaining. The Yeti, a typical Smithers Jones character, regimented bowler hat and pinstriped togs every day with briefcase and brolly on permanent stand-bye, had a 60's Beatles wig stuck on his face. His birds' nest of a beard and adjoining tash showed no space for a mouth. With a head framed by two dead rabbits for sideburns, and a bowler hat to top the fuzzy mess, you could barely see his eyes or skin. The Pinstriped Yeti having no visible face made him leap a little from the multitudes.

Another, The Ski Instructor, wore clown or court Jester type footwear, with his shoes being way-out in front and curled up at the toe. Paddy joked his feet were heeled in Aberdeen, ankled in Birmingham and toe-ended in London. An on-site wager that no man, no matter how hard he tried, could get the attention of The Ski Instructor was set. Shout or give him the verbal's, he'd remain cool as a Vegas poker king, not change face and carry on taking those gigantic strides of his as he footslogged to work. After weeks of relentless provocation, by a gang of building workers with nothing better to do, The Ski Instructor – Tugboat Toes with the biggest socks in the world – could not be unnerved. He was renamed Mr. Granite, the one whose feathers could not be ruffled, and insults were replaced with bowing in front of him whenever he showed face. The morning he finally raised a smile brightened our day no end and the fella became a bit of a hero. I suppose there's a message in there somewhere.

The site held the usual suspects: Irish navvies, a few more Scouse brickies and labourers, other Northerners and Jocks, and finally, the main body of workers, Southerners, with a number of Cockneys thrown in the cement mix. To me, the suits walking past each day were the Foot Soldiers of Miserable Margaret's Tory enemy; making me the worst for shouting abuse, or throwing buckets of water or big handfuls of soil over the fence. Sometimes I'd go into work armed with boxes of eggs. Boney would notice. 'Fried eggs this week then, eh?'

'Nah, me and Paddy's gonna have some scrambled, Bone.'

'Oh! Scrambled eggs eh Mickey?'

'Nah…scrambled heads!'

Up the scaffold, seven floors up, I had a grandstand view of the Suit Soldiers pouring out of the tube and mainline station. I made a small hidey-hole behind some planks of wood, where you could go for a ten minute skive or bomb away with dairy produce. Once the worker ants emerged into daylight from station exits to another morning at the office, I'd be lobbing eggs to the centre of any main group of briefcases and umbrella's. They'd be looking skyward, as if to say, *my god, haven't those bloody pigeons got nests to lay eggs in?*

Seriously bored, deranged or, unquestionably bitter, however you look at it, I thought it was a good laugh; and, in my own cauliflower logic, thought it was a blow against the Tory, Yuppie scumbags who seemed to have everything their own way. I'd watch them, briefcases to the floor, running hands through hair, looking to the heavens thinking the seagull and pigeon Luftwaffe were in town for the day. A Cockney lad, Jamie, a Bricklayer from Stratford, would join me for the devilment and throw the eggs with more venom than me or Paddy; stating, 'Listen Scouse, I hate these Yuppie Wankers as much as you!'

The angry young men infrequently performing this prank never once thought of the injury or pain it could cause, or the consequences that could arise from fingerprints on shells… sort of, eggs as evidence. Soon it escalated to throwing spade-full's of soil over the high perimeter fence. Office-bods would shout back. 'Hey you, you bloody nutcase, what's going on?' One morning, this huge, 'ripped and muscled' merchant came around the fence dressed in a worker ant, double-breasted, pinstripe suit. With neck muscles bursting above his shirt collar, like they'd formed a dam keeping the blood in his head, it gave him a Hammerhead shark appearance. Same as Whitelaw's bodyguards, he'd been carrying carpets all his life. It got me picturing myself as an old rug, carpet carried off-site to have the dust beaten out of me. The fella raged. 'Somebody or something has just thrown soil all over my new suit, and somebody or something is going to have to pay!'

'Happens all the time mate, yer can't do fuck all about that!' I offered.

'Oh, we have a Northerner in our midst do we? My grandfather was from Liverpool, and he left the grimy place to get away from mucky little beggars like you!'

Cupping his hand like a digging machine, he scooped a large handful of soil and threw it…splat! Bang into my face! It was in my eyes, mouth, hair, *Bastard*! My eyes were stinging immediately. Chewing soil, but lost for words anyway, I'd been stun-gunned!

About eight fellers stood monitoring proceedings, till the rising rumble of the ol' red mist began to cloud East London. Bending to scoop handfuls of dirt, clicked me into human windmill mode. Lobbing as much as possible, muscleman made an easy target. Paddy joined in, as a couple of other lads threw sly handfuls. Before anybody could apologize it all turned Keystone Cops, only more serious. Hammerhead chased about the site trying to catch me. He wouldn't have caught me if he'd have tried all night. Vinny, an older Cockney guy, stepped in. 'Come on mister; take it easy, this is going nowhere.'

'Fuck off you old cunt! Get out of my way!' Hammerhead growled, pushing Vinny's hands away. Vinny, who we'd nicknamed Alf Ramsey because of a likeness to the old England manager, picked up a spade and went to maim him, till another fella, Joey Barcelona (he had a Spanish surname nobody could pronounce), grabbed it before it connected with his bulging forehead. By now all of us were throwing dirt at him but, it was the shovel attack that made him back off. Backing toward the gate, with rubble and soil belting down on him, he's shouting 'I'll be back with a firm later; you'll see!'

Once it stopped, I walked to the gate and shouted 'If your Grandad was from Liverpool, he must've been the only Hammerhead shark to swim the Mersey.'

'What the fuck is wrong with you?' He screamed, before steaming at me again. Catching me unaware with a flying rugby tackle – hey ho – its Keystone Cops again! Being so big, I'm thinking; *stay close, don't catch one of those haymakers he's throwing*. We rolled about on the floor for what seemed like ages, but probably no longer than twenty seconds. He wasn't getting any punches off. Meantime, trying to rub muck into his face, I couldn't get higher than the rim of his shirt collar. The site lads jumped in and stopped it. Releasing his grip, I unfairly let fly with another handful of dirt. It hit his face with such force it rocked him a little. A Mexican stand-off ensued, with the two of us stood munching soil. I'd reached the stage where I had no fear of police intervention, or whatever was to arise. I knew I'd been out of order but this fella was a complete fucking pinstriped loon and, sometimes, the only way to face up to a loon was to act the part yourself.

Once the lads cooled things and shark features walked off, I sneaked out the back gate with a pickaxe handle, caught him up, and said, 'Listen mate, alright, it was me. If there's gonna be comebacks, gerron with it now.'

I didn't fancy looking over my shoulder for weeks on end. It was bad enough living at the bedsit and being a Labourer every day, never mind having to worry about a shark attack from behind when digging a hole. The guy looked me up and down. You could see he'd sensed I was deadly serious. He reverted to sensible Southern businessman mode. 'Look sonny-Jim; I'm from an ordinary working background, probably like yourself. Don't let the suit fool you. Day in, day out, I go to a job I detest big-time and sometimes the merest thing can tip the balance over the edge. Today's sure looking like one of them days; so why don't you piss off back to your building site and let me get on with my fucked-up life!'

The veins in his neck, ready to pop, he spelled the final sentence. 'Can you twig exactly where I'm coming from? Ay… can ya?'

The guy's demeanor had changed again; dramatically. His accent, coarser, he didn't sound or look right in his soiled pinstripe suit. For the briefest, I almost felt sorry for him, only he'd just told me to piss off. 'Ok. Mate, I get where yer coming from.'

As he walked, I'm thinking, *different suit than me; better paying job; more money; richer lifestyle – contrasting set of problems!* It didn't matter what part of the tree you lived, the pressure could mount whatever the lifestyle. Outward signs said: successful businessman; fit and able bodied; tanned and wealthy. But, rubbed the wrong way, scratched below the surface, and the grief, bubbling underneath...left on the same low light as mine, simmered away, sitting there, sitting and waiting...ready to explode!

The suit had that disparaging, empty, cold look in his eyes; like a Ninja-Turtle-heroin-addict zooming in for his next brain wallop! The soil in his hair, face and suit made its contribution towards an addict-like appearance; but no way was Hammerhead from the scruffy, street-grafters side of the needle tracks. Though he had that 'gone-on-the-gear', far-off-look you see them modelling, this guy's fix must've been money, materialism and keeping up with the Jones's. Suit and bulging frame apart, his face and actions showed that same jaded, fucked-up manner!

Life's lessons were getting learnt daily. Though I hated the Tory Shysters who ran the country, and all those who voted and supported them with loving greed, nailed-on Tories like Hammerhead had me questioning a lot of my stereotypes and the things I took for gospel. The way he hadn't thought twice about fighting all and sundry in the building yard, allied to the hollow grey eyes and bursting neck vessels, told me this was one deeply disturbed worker ant. Were other worker ants feeling like him? Leaving the yard to confront him with a pickaxe handle was a waste of time really...I mean, I still ended up looking over my shoulder for the next few weeks. Whereas only recently I'd envied them their status and lifestyle prospects, it wasn't taking long to click that there was no way I wanted to live like them.

6

COMFORTABLY NUMB
THE SHOPLIFTING LIFESTYLE BEGINS IN EARNEST.

Phoning family to tell them I was coming home for the weekend, my Da said he would take great pleasure in toe-ending my brother back to his own bedroom as he'd been spending far too long on the sign-on treadmill and in my ex-flock. Telling Bilko not to pencil us in for overtime, we looked forward to a weekend home and a well-earned blowout. He agreed, providing he had labour cover. Covered or not, we were offski. Friday afternoon he approached to ask when we'd be making tracks.

'Half an hour before the four o'clock train.' I offered. The other two pushed me as spokesperson. It felt comfortable; till Boney started bugging me on the hour to ask Bilko if it was ok to have a brew, a break, a piss…

'Mickey, go an' ask Bilko shall I start digging' them footings?'

'Mickey, it's nearly dinner, ask Bilko can I shoot out for some scoff?'

This is all-day, everyday, till time to tube it to McRent's. 'Mickey, we're not that busy, ask Bilko can we have an early dart?'

'Can't you go over Bone? You've been on the site longer than me.'

'I know that Mickey, but you know how to ask. Go on, ask for us.'

Come Friday, he's at me again. 'Mickey, tell Bilko were getting' an earlier train; he'll be alright.'

'Look Boney, if you think Bilko's gonna be alright, tell him yourself.'

'Ah eh Mickey, you've got the right patter.'

'Listen Ralph McTell, if you can find your way round the streets of London with no tube map, then you can find you way to Bilko's site hut no problem!'

Predictably, come eleven o'clock, I spoke to Bernie. 'Listen, if me and the lads get stuck in for a couple of hours, and everything's ship-shape, what's the chance of leaving' early to catch the one or two o'clock from Euston Bernie?'

'As long as it's not an every week occurrence and all your jobs are finished, it should be okay, Mickey. Everything's got to be tidied away mind you, so the lads coming in tomorrow won't have any difficulty finding tools and stuff.'

We got stuck into digging footings so concrete could be poured before Brickies got to work. Even professional skiver Paddy dug with the same gusto as Boney and me. Soon enough it seemed the Foreman was on his way over with the wages.

'Paddy, Boney here we go; Bilko's on his way over.'

Shifting soil like two gravediggers an hour before the funeral, they stopped as Bilko approached. 'Ok lads, listen-up. Its twelve thirty, I know you've been getting stuck-in. I've got no problem with you leaving early. Thing is, you might have to hang on anyway, the wages haven't arrived yet.'

The Yuppie building boss usually brought the wages around eleven or twelve. He'd been late before. Usual scenario, I'm thinking: *love making money, but boy, do they hate giving it away!* As Bilko walked off, Paddy snarled. 'I knew that snooty, yuppie wanker would be late! Acting the Prince in his little, red corvette! Probably having tea and biscuits at the Savoy.'

We caught sight of boss's son, James Brumble, occasionally. He delivered wages in a brand new red Jag for his father's property development firm. According to the Bricklaying gangs who'd worked for the company a while, young Brumble, 30'ish, spent Friday scooting around various London building sites dropping off bags of cash for employees. Bilko said he'd annoyingly beep the horn of his snazzy car outside the site gates every Friday. 'Snooty little bastard won't even open the car door!'

Knowing it was Brumble he'd take time answering the din. James Brumble took no interest in work progress, or people on site. We reckoned he didn't like getting his tasty Russell and Bromley shoes dirty, and was terrified of getting robbed if he strayed from the car. Boney, trying to focus on an advertisement for a new pop-single, *Papa Don't Preach* by Madonna, squinted, saying, 'Eyes on Bilko, he probably thinks Brumble's driving Noddy's red truck, or a London bus.'

Paddy laughed. 'You've gorra cheek don't yer' think? Fucksake, between you, Bernie and Stevie Wonder you could start the Wonky Wall Building Company!'

Straightening up, he brushed soil from his clothing. 'The newspaper ad could read: From groundwork to roof tile, we promise to build your dream home on totally the wrong piece of land!'

Boney raised a smile. Digging some more, I said to Paddy. 'You've blimped the paymaster most, what's he like then?'

'A bit of a Dudley Moore, crossed with Prince, with a little bit of Reg Varney, early-days On the Busses thrown in.'

His explanation had me creased. We settled for a cherubic-faced little Yuppie with a mop of black hair. A youngish Del Boy…maybe…details, whatever!

'Where the fuck's Brumble?' Jamie, the local brickie interrupted us.

Agitated, I realized we'd missed the one and probably the two o'clock train. Walking to the hut, I found Bilko polishing his glasses. 'Best getting a window cleaner on those Bernard. Any sign of the cash yet?'

'I'll let you know quick as I can…Promise'

I told the lads I thought the two o'clock train looked a no-no. 'I knew we wouldn't get off early. He's probably got the wages under the table and wants more graft.' Paddy ventured.

Not wanting to wait about we continued digging. Half one, Bilko came over. 'Listen Mickey, come the hut a minute, I might be able to help out.'

Hoping the wages had arrived or were in transit, I walked behind him. 'If you lads are in a rush, how about I give you a personal cheque right now; pop it in your own bank account and pay the lads yourself.'

'There's nothing like the ol' cash in hand Bernie. I've never been paid by cheque before. I don't think the lads'll be too keen. Appreciate the offer anyway.'

'Go and see what they think. I've heard nothing from Brumble. I know you lads are keen to go home. A cheque won't cause you any aggravation Mickey, as long as you can cover the lad's weekend money. That way you can leave for Euston right now…Put it into your own account. In a few days it'll have cleared.'

'I see what yer' saying. Let me speak to Paddy and Boney; see what they think.'

Walking across site a Level 42 song boomed from a battered, old, Drain Layer's radio, *'Because there's something about you, baby, so right'*. The drains firm, West Country boys, had a main grafter who was a Johnny Rotten ringer. I hollered into the ditch. 'Wharrabout some Pistols Johnny' with Boney screaming over 'Fuck all that, wharrabout the wages? Come on Mickey, we off or what?'

'Brumble's still missing Bone, but Bilko's told me he can give us a cheque so we can get straight off. What d'you'se think?'

'How d'ya mean a cheque…a company cheque, a personal cheque?'

'He said a cheque from his own account. I'll have to cover it, though.'

'Have yer' got the dough Mickey?' Boney pleaded, while shouting, 'Ay, turn that fucken' radio down!'

'Suppose so. I've got what I was taking home, plus spend's: about seven hundred quid. I know we were due two-fifty wages, but I could give you one fifty-each and the rest when the cheques cleared. I'm in shit-street if Bilko's cheques a dud, though.'

'Bernie's sound. Come on lets skedaddle. A hundred and fifty nicker'll do me till Monday. That horse romped home yesterday. I'm sixty quid up already.'

'Slow down Boney lad, wharrabout you Paddy?'

Before he could speak, Boney jumped in again. Come on Paddy, we're wasting time. Bernie's sound, he'll never let us down.'

'Shurrup Boney, I've heard your fucken' *sound* before! Well...Paddy?'

'It's up to you Mickey. It's your dough.'

'I'll front the one-fifty each, but you'll get the rest when the cheques through.'

'Fair enough; let's go. If yer' get the cheque we can still make the two o'clock.'

An upbeat Paddy was all the encouragement I needed. I knew I wouldn't make the Bank. Fresh off the boat concerning Bank's, and especially cheques, my knowledge went as far as: it opened till three o'clock each day, and you could stash unspent money from the weekend's blowout in an account there. Getting a Friday special home, returning Sunday evening meant the cheque wouldn't reach my Big Time Charlie account till Monday's visit. Bernie had to clarify the cheque would still be valid, though only two or three days old. In my naivety, I thought it had to be deposited the day it was written.

Choco-block with building site workers, returning home flush with wedge, Friday's trains to Liverpool had become notorious parties on wheels. The 'Cattle truck', the 'Party in Motion' and the 'Ale on the Rail' partied North on the hour every Friday afternoon and, we wanted on! Bernie wrote the cheque. Hurtling into the bowels of the tube station we caught a Hammersmith bound tube, alighting at Euston Square. Galloping from the Station, I'm thinking about the little Pakistani kid with the Colgate smile, before racing like a speedball to the heart of Euston Station…only to find we'd missed the Liverpool train by a couple of minutes. We had an hour to kill. Not to be deterred, we got the party underway in the Gardeners Arms, a small boozer outside the mainline station. Forty minutes later, we bought twenty-four cans of ale and four bottles of wine. It doesn't take a genius to work out that by the time we got to Liverpool Lime Street we stepped off the train like newborn horse triplets.

Landing on the Liverpool pavement I became ultra-aware of the strong smell of the sea, something you only notice when you've been inland for a while. I've come out of that station as drunk as any eucalyptus-chomping Koala Bear, as sober as a Hare Krishna meditating at a quiet mountain retreat, and as tired as a Roman Foot Soldier with tattered sandals, but, no matter what state I've been in, that salty smell has always hit me like a lead weight. It made you want to run out of Lime Street all the way down the hill and dive straight into the Mersey. Thing is, you knew you'd only get torpedoed back out of the water by one of those little brown submarines.

Usually, out on the gargle, I'm staying out! That night, I was tucked-up by one o'clock in the morning. Though drunk, I spread out star-shaped to try and cover every inch of the mattress. Feeling like a one-inch kangaroo snuggled in its mother's huge pouch, going to sleep never felt so good. For the first time in two months I listened to the sound of silence, with no farts, no snores, and only the soothing notes of *Dark Side of the Moon* to send me floating into the cosmos. And, isn't it funny how you think you're missing out on what's going on back home when you've been away for a while, only to return to find you've missed sweet FA. Same people, same old dance. Family were fine, health wise, but still signing-on and eking out a living. My Ma and Da gave me no grief about the steel stockholder's, especially when they could see I was in fine fettle and earning decent dough. My Da did pull me aside, to say, 'Don't start getting up to any cowboy capers, or daft scams. We don't want Bizzies on this doorstep, d'yer' hear what I'm saying?'

My Ma had always told me about good and bad Karma, and John Lennon singing about 'Instant Karma', how good be-gets good and bad be-gets bad. Thinking about hard-up local people with morals like my Ma and Da, and filthy rich Tories with hardly any, along with being young, had me thinking it all sounded a bit airy-fairy. Their honesty was admirable, but I'd seen the filthy rich strutting their stuff round London with their bellies full, and I already knew that equality and quality of life in this system came at a price, and a risk.

A few of my old mates came out on the Saturday night. We ended up singing along to the Clash, Big Audio Dynamite and the Jam songs that littered jukebox's at our favourite boozers in town. Good vibes abounded as I bounced past George Henry's department store thinking of Dennis with the eyebrows, and around old stomping ground with cash to burn. The fantastic smell of the sea permeated every pub doorway, and wafted its way down piss-stained back-alleys. Good days and nights, loose and carefree, out on the wallop in Sailortown.

A lot of Liverpool workers, ensconced in the warmth and familiarity of their own abodes, found it hard to up-sticks for the return journey back to Moneyville. I have to say that with my Ma's cooking and that darling of a mattress, like those family men, my own new moneymaking career almost collapsed into the pillow that weekend. But, being a man on a mission, a man on *the* up, to give in and lie down had no place on my new self-help agenda.

'Paddy, where's dozy-hole, any sign?'

'He phoned our house earlier, said there'd be no problem.'

It was quarter-to-six, Sunday evening, with Lime Street station full of migrant workers making their way back to London. These trains, as raucous as the Friday specials, had Transport Bizzies on full alert. Feller's too rowdy to travel got ejected before it left the buffers. Though never as joyful a journey as the ride back home, usually a Sunday night cram-it-in mentality meant the journey back to London became a worse booze cruise than Friday's expedition.

'Here's Mophead now!'

'Come on soft-lad, it's leaving in a minute!'

'How many cans have you two got?'

'We've got twenty four, that'll be enough.'

Too late for off-licence excursions, we boarded at Platform eight. Normal bunking strategy didn't have to be deployed. We'd picked up cheap tickets for the return journey. People travelling one-way from London to Liverpool bought unwanted return tickets, being cheaper than a one-way single at Euston. Unwanted return tickets went to the guard, who would pocket as many valid returns as possible. The guard, enterprisingly pitching himself at Lime Street station, Sunday evening, sold the returns to people like us. Setting up this scam, he not only supplemented his own shitty wages, but also provided a great service for people who only worked away in the first place due to lack of cash. To older family men who found bunking a hindrance, he was a man in esteem – a godsend!

Those same fellers formed a queue outside Lime Street station on a warm, sunny Sunday evening. Standing, cash in hand, they shouted, 'Here's the guard, quick, here's the guard!' The only thing skimmed from? The British Rail Bank account, and, I mean, who gives a flying fuck about that! With their million pound pay-offs for early retiring managers…Ha!

Disembarking at Euston, we Northern Line tube'd it to

Tottenham Court Road, changing to the Central Line bound for Hainault. Finished with trains at Gants Hill, Paddy goes, 'Strange feeling to be here. I was sitting in the living room with me Ma and Da a few hours ago. Back in Timbuk-fucken-tu again! It's like we live half our lives to-ing and fro-ing on bleeding' trains!'

'Par for the course brother,' I replied. Adding, 'Far as I'm concerned that's the way it's gonna be till I make the trip home with something substantial in me bin!'

Boney piped up. 'I won't be going home anymore. I saw enough at the weekend to tell me that. There's nothing back home for me. No hope, no job, no dough, nothing! Anymore, count me out. I'm staying put!'

True to his word, he never travelled north for years. And, only when desperate to see family or in need of a change from the shitty sleeping arrangements at McRents, did Paddy and I return. Reaching the door, a sign stood in the front garden 'Flat to let'. 'That's the one for me. I'm down the Social tomorrow to get the rent sorted.'

Overdue my own gaff, I laid claim to the vacancy. Boney opened the door to the sight of Miserable Tits necking away with her new Lesbian Lollipop. Paddy popped his head over Boney's shoulder. 'Aye Aye, rules of the house? Gerrin' yer' own room will yer. This is a communal area, not a place for two men to be snogging!'

She moved away from the much smaller girl. 'You dirty, horrible, Irish twats! Come on Siobhan; don't listen to these idiotic, male chauvinist pigs!'

She trounced upstairs, bringing her massive, denim-clad-arse into view. Her pint-sized, skinny girlfriend looked like Olive Oil compared to Pluto in blue jeans. 'Irish twats...male chauvinist pigs...what the fuck's she on about? Paddy enquired.

'Take no notice; she's not the full shilling that soft cow!' Boney offered.

She looked over her shoulder back down the stairs, growling 'Don't you dare call me a cow…You fucking Irish pig?'

Not in the mood, I returned the growl. 'Ahh go and get Olive Oil to shave your minge, Mister fucken' misery!'

Paddy childishly began chanting…

'Go and get Siobhan, to get the razor, on y'lawn!'

'Go and get Siobhan, to get the razor, on y'lawn!'

Worse, we all joined in. The Raincoat Jocks, hearing the commotion, opened their rehearsal room door to join in. Gavin, one of the keyboard kings, came around the door wearing a pair of threadbare, yellowy-white, Y-fronts, white tennis socks, with a long, grey mac framing his scraggy white belly. We were in pleats before he spoke, 'I cannae fucken' stand that cranky dyke!'

Barry White appeared with his horror film laugh; bit like an axe murderer on fifty smokes a day. Then, in a heavy Jamaican accent, Clifford, the seven-foot Rasta shouted downstairs. 'What's all the bloody noise man?'

Peeping over the balustrade, he worked out what was happening, smiled and slowly walked back to his room as wads of ganja smoke billowed onto the landing. It was a scene from 'The Young Ones' with Boney as Neil the hippy, Paddy and myself were Rik and Vivian, Clifford was Mike, the serious one in black who didn't get involved; Barry White was Alexei Sayle paying a brief visit, and the Scotch lads were the weekly guests. It became more surreal when Gavin shot back into his room to get a rhythm going on the keyboards. The words changed.

'Go and get Siobhan, ch ch, ch,

To come and shave y'lawn, clap, clap, clap,

Clifford reappeared over the bannister amid a huge cloud of smoke 'Ok feller's, I can't hear me music.'

His toothless grin gradually faded the scene. With everyone locked behind bedsit doors I thought of farmyard animals dying to escape, wanting a glimpse of life on the outside, only to realize it was hopeless, and that that bit of real life they'd just encountered could never last...Time to get back to the cages.

My own reality of another night of Boney farting and snoring into his crusty blankets hit me. Oh well, it was his Chicken Coop. Nearest the door, I heard the muffled sounds of Siobhan and Miserable Tits canoodling. I drifted off wondering what tastier Lesbians got upto? But the next door image of legendary wrestler, Mick McManus grappling away with Popeye's Olive Oil kept coming to mind. With no sexual mileage in that one I luckily nodded off to sleep; the ale, as always, my haze, my saviour, my knockout drop.

Getting slam-dunked...sorry, dropped back into the land of snores and brown smoke, had me rising even earlier. The window, constantly ajar, got opened to the full no matter what the weather. With the other two moaning about draught and traffic noise I often jumped an early tube to get some fresh air. Viewing crack-of-dawn-workers, like the market people around Spitalfields, I'd catch a glance from one of them wondering why I was staring over at that ungodly hour. I'd think of my brother's and the thousands of other jobless people still in bed, gagging for a day's work like these people. Any patriotism I may have shown towards my country when growing up was hastily being nailed-down in a coffin for early burial, deep within the London soil I now walked.

'Paddy, Boney, come on, rise and shine, time to go.'

Paddy stretched and yawned. 'Yeah, let's go, it stinks of Boney's undies in here.'

'Oh yeah, and I suppose you fart pink air freshener then!' Boney countered.

Needing out, I interrupted the morning banter. 'If we leave now, we can have an early brekkie in that little café off Commercial Street by the Market.'

Three full-English's later, we took a slow meandering walk to the building site to let the food digest. From a distance I noticed Brumble's red Jag. 'He's a bit fucken' late with the wages!'

Paddy stopped. 'It's not like Brumbleballs to be on site early doors. He's speaking to arl Vinny, maybe Bilko hasn't showed up yet. It's not like him to be late.'

As we approached, Vinny spoke. 'Alright boys, you'se didn't see any cheques from Bernie Tomlinson on the Friday, did'ya?'

'Yeah, we did...why? Go on, what's the story Vinny?' I asked. 'Wharrever you're gonna say, don't tell us he's pissed off back to Middlesborough to open an opticians with our dough, that's all?'

'Sorry t'say this...but that might be the case fellers.'

'Agh, tell me yer kidding Vinny!'

'Nah, fraid it looks that way Mickey. Yersee, apparently Friday afternoon he's gone an' told about twelve lads that Mr. Brumble here hadn't arrived with the wages yet, and asked them would they take personal cheques from himself, till he knew the score. Mr.Brumble brought the wages early on Friday, so it looks like this Arsehole has ripped-off quite a few of the guys on site and, err...apparently you three by the sounds of it. Mr. Brumble can't believe it. This guy has been with the Brumble's a couple of years now. With his site know-ledge and age seniority he was basically left in a trustworthy position, which, it looks certain he's abused.'

'Twelve feller's, that's roughly four or five grand isn't it?' Paddy asked.

'I've got the cheque in me pocket here now. I was gonna throw it in the bank around break-time.'

Brumble took the cheque from my hand. 'The Police will have to have a look at this. Do you mind if I hold on to it with the others?'

'Nah, its fucken' toilet paper to me now...pardon my French!'

Boney woke up. 'Wharrabout the job then...we getting back to work, or are we finished-up or what?'

My brain felt skewered. I'd not only lost a week's wages, I doubted I'd see the £300 I'd given to Boney and Paddy. The two of them, always a week behind, would be back even further. Though 'wage-rip' had happened to me before it was a scenario you'd never get used to. If anything, it felt worse each time. I couldn't help think, *not again!* Just as you're gliding along, drifting nicely on life's ocean, why does some dirty, sneaky bastard of an iceberg always come from nowhere to smash into your hull, sending you shit-faced to rock bottom?

Credit due, Brumble offered. 'Listen guys, start work when you like. Take the morning off if need be, sort your finances out. If you want to work today that's totally up to you. I'll tell you guys without hesitation that this has happened before on one of my Father's building sites, and will no doubt happen again on other building sites. But, I stress, it will not be happening again within this Company. I'll be paying the wages myself personally from here on in.'

I'm thinking: *once somebody realizes how much money this fella's carrying, it'll be a large scale wage-rip soon!* The bit about finances had me smirking. I mean, finances…at Boney's bank safe bedsit – Ha! I put a new tuneless mantra hastily in place, *never, trust anyone, again!* It might not seem like a lot of money, or a big deal, but it was to me. Everything happens for a reason, an' all that. Well, I had a life-defining lesson carved into my brain the day that four-eyed Foreman took a hike with our wages. Never again would I rely on anybody to feed or clothe me in any way whatsoever. From thereon in, any money in pocket would come from my own endeavours. Time had arrived to maximize earning capability using my own nous. First step, take power out of the employers' hands and put it firmly and directly into mine. The emphasis needed to be on me – only me; no employer, no Social, no handouts, just me.

In one way I suppose I owe Bernie 'Bilko' Tomlinson for the dough he stole from us, seeing as he helped empower me. I believe that what happened next, and from then on, you could trace directly back to that one act of human selfishness. True, I already had small time government, social and light fingered issues, but, I mean, that bastard! In honesty, I hoped he choked to death. Then again, suppose I'm wasting time writing these few words. That fella was never gonna read this with those eyes.

After calling the four-eyed wage-snatcher every name under the sun, I realized it was no good crying all day over pay packets gone-north-east. 'I don't know what you'ze wanna do, but I'm gonna sort that flat out for meself. I couldn't face working this morning. Maybe this afternoon'll be alright, maybe tomorrow, who knows?'

Paddy answered. 'I'm coming with you Mickey; me hearts not in it this morning. Wharrabout you Bone?'

'Nah, I'm staying put. Fuck all for me out there. Might as well get me head down and get to work.'

Confirming we'd be back that afternoon, Vinny offered, 'I know yer' heads are wrecked, but don't spew it. I'll be running the site from now on and things will run a lot better for us now, you'll see.'

Walking away from site, Paddy explained Vinny was from Canning Town, and reckoned he was a sound fella. I warned him about the *sound* word and making Boney-type assumptions.

'I know, but yer' can't blame Boney for what's happened.'

'Course not. But he uses that word way too freely. It's me own fault for listening to the dozy bastard anyway. It won't happen again.'

'Mickey, hang on a sec…What d'yer'reckons going on here then?'

Another Next shop looked to be opening up as we walked by. They were sprouting up all over the place. It was nine o'clock in the morning. Shop-staff marched boxes full of clothing from lorry to shop. Paddy, intrigued, reckoned each time the last person entered the premises they left no one guarding the truck. 'What d'yer' think Mickey?'

'Well, we look a bit scruffy, but it looks a goer.'

We stood across the road and watched. Every fourth person that disappeared into the shop left the lorry unattended for twenty to thirty seconds. 'Paddy, box each, straight down that jigger. Anyone pulls us, act daft, like we're trying to help; then give it serious toes!'

Crossing through busy traffic, we raced up the ramp, box each then straight down the back jigger a few doors down. It went smoothly. Becoming hard-faced, Paddy motioned. 'Yersee this back-alley, it comes out by our site.'

'Yer' kidding, how d'yer' know that?'

'I've been getting a grip of that bird down here lunchtime. Anyway, I'll tell yer' later; another box or what?'

'Yeah…why not, come on, get on with it.'

Leaving the jigger, we crossed the road to watch the lorry being unloaded. Surveying the street came back affirmative. With nobody clocking us Paddy began counting people back into the shop. 'That's the first one, second girl, third. Here's the fella at the back in the gigs, yeah, go on lad, fuck off inside!'

I confirmed he was last one in. 'Ok. In now, it's laughing. After you Sir.'

We giggled like stupid school kids; one of those nervous laughs emanating from a shady bit of skullduggery that can easily go tits up. Paddy pointed at what to take. 'Get that box over there that says pants.'

'Right you are Sir.'

Down the ramp, quick, quick, quick and straight up the alley, slow, slow, slow. Paddy stopped to put his box down. 'What's all this Sir business?'

'Why…got a problem with it?'

'No, I like it. I could get used to it.'

We laughed like a pair of dim-wits again.

'What d'yer' reckon Paddy, one more box each or what?'

'How're we gonna lug these?'

'Never mind that…one more or what?'

'It's up to you.'

'Fuck it, come on, last trip.'

Walking from the alleyway I tried scanning the whole street. Not easy with people rushing to work and vans being unloaded at other shops. Suddenly a Plod car sped by, stopping the two of us in our tracks. 'Last one deffo...Ok Paddy.'

'Spew it now if you want? Boxes are getting low anyway.'

'Nah, come on, last one for us.'

We stood on the other side of the road, counting in unison. One...two...three...four, knock at the door. Let's go!'

Walking up the steep ramp you could see the back of the last guy to leave the lorry as he made his way into the bowels of the shop carrying one of the boxes. Walking back down the ramp, I said good morning to a nosey old lady. She didn't acknowledge my gesture. Glancing back over her shoulder, she walked bandily on her way, with me thinking about John Wayne's sister. Before boxes five and six were stacked I realized I was sweating. 'Now's the hard part; it's not gonna be easy lugging these.'

The dopey laugh kicked-in again. Come on soft lad; get a move on, what direction?'

Paddy pointed right. 'It's about a hundred yards down there.'

The back-jigger went in a semi-circle. You couldn't see around each bend; meaning: you couldn't see into the distance to tell if someone was ahead, behind or creeping up on your tail. Paddy, marching behind me, was laughing, speaking and tugging for breaths all at the same time. 'Fucksake...these are getting heavy!'

'Shut up for a second Muscles...How far now?'

'It's around this bend; fucksake, me arms'll be like Mighty Joe Young's.'

Laughing again, I dropped the box. 'Paddy, run ahead; I'll wait here. Get Boney and arl Vinny.'

'No! Come on Mickey, I'll shut-up now, honest. Don't stop! It's not far; we'll bring them back with us.'

'What d'yer' reckon on arl Vinny, Paddy? I know Boney's Ok. But...'

'Nah, Vinny's a sound fella Mickey.'

'Don't use that fucken' word I've told yer!'

'Alright, alright; take it easy narky knickers!'

Light shining through the next opening between buildings got me hoping it was the one leading to the Site. 'Paddy, this the one or what?'

'I'm sure this is it, yeh!'

Two trucks loaded with brick blocked most of the site entrance, ideal for creating an obstructed view. Any on site nosey-parkers would have us down as unloading boxes from the trucks. 'After you Sir.' I let Paddy go first, allowing me a final gander at the surrounding area or any passing busy-bodies. I gave him the Ok.

'Everything's sweet. Get to the office big balls.'

Paddy pushed at the hut door. It swung open as he let go of the handle. The ground, muddy with tyre tracks from delivery and machinery traffic, meant the hut was a dry, clean sanctuary. Plopping the boxes down, I motioned to Paddy. 'Quick, go and get Vinny, I'll get Boney.'

Catching sight of Boney, he pretended to look busy. He couldn't skive right.

'Alright Mickey, where's Paddy? Thought you'ze were gonna sort that flat out?'

'Never mind that Bone, I've gorra job for yer! Come on, follow me.'

'Since when've you been the boss? I've got work to do here.'

'Boney, shut the fuck up! Follow me dickhead!'

'Alright, alright, take it easy!'

We could see Paddy with Vinny in tow. Funny...nobody spoke. Getting in line, we played follow the leader. Paddy,

Olympic style: bum cheeks to the east, bum cheeks to the west, marched on. They entered the alleyway by the entrance Paddy and I had used. I kept distance for a quick street scan. Once I'd glanced proceedings surrounding the site entrance, I made headway down the jigger. By the time I caught up they were on their way back laden with boxes. Vinny winked toward me. 'Quite heavy, should be a nice bit of boodle.'

I caught Paddy's eye. 'You checked your walk? Yer' walking like a farmyard rooster on speed! Are all the boxes still in place?'

'Yeah, yeh they're all there.'

Each of the six boxes got carried the length of the jigger before being dispatched to Vinny's hidey hut. From labelling, we noticed one of the boxes contained fifteen shirts. We assumed the other three, also marked shirts, contained likewise. A gentle opening of a shirt box, followed by a rough count, confirmed this. We found the two trouser boxes contained fifteen pairs of formal pants each. Verified, Vinny, sweating like Alf Ramsey in 66, chirped, 'Should be around nine hundred nicker here lads?'

'How d'yer' work that one out Vinn?' I asked.

'Well…should be no problem getting ten spots on each item. Ninety items, tenner a go: nine hundred quid.'

'So, d'yer' know anyone who can do them for us Vinny?'

'Shouldn't be a problem; probably do them meself. Listen, take me about two weeks tops to do them all in. Or, if you want, howzabout I give you eight hundred this afternoon, no questions. What d'yer' say boys?'

'Open another box Vinny; let's have a gander at the gear.' Paddy asked.

'Yeah, I was gonna have a blimp anyway. Don't want anything from Liberace's wardrobe do we?'

He peeled back the cardboard on one of the boxes: simple white dress shirts, with a light, sky blue check. Then, wafer-thin, grey cotton pants. Taking a look into the final box, Vinny confirmed his offer. 'Yeah, it's up to you fellers, no problem, eight hundred this afternoon or nine in a couple of weeks.'

Sounded like quick money to me. 'Eight this savvy'll be alright Vin. Yer' know, bit of fast-track compensation for last week's wages.'

Vinny agreed. 'Listen boys, any more of this gear and I'll take it all day.'

'Cheers for that Vinny. Come on Paddy lad; you still coming with me or what?'

'Yeah, come on.'

'See yer' later Bone.'

'Yeah, catch yer' later Mickey. Tara Paddy lad.'

Walking off site I'm elbowing Paddy. 'Nice touch that mate. Me head woulda' been cabbaged all week without that bit of dough turning up.'

'It's like a roller-coaster this. I'm feeling numb. Eight hundred nicker in half an hour, decent money that Mickey. How're we gonna split it? We gonna give Boney a dropsy or what?'

'Course we are. If I take me three hundred quid out, it'll leave five. Two hundred each for me and you, and we'll give Boney a ton. You comfortable with that?'

'Yeah, sound as.'

'Paddy, d'yer' have to say that word? Listen, I'll ask Vinny what he makes on that bit of clobber. I'm sure he'll tell us straight-up what profit he's made. If it's not much we'll drop him a nifty between us. Best keep him sweet. He sounded like he knew the score, and I've gorra feeling we'll need him again.'

Paddy turned with a daft grin on his face. 'Hope yer' right. Mind you, it's like the ol' cliché: it's not often a load of swag falls off the back of a lorry, is it?'

Away from Site, I jumped into a phone box and belled Boneys landlord. Asking about the spare flat, McRent told me he'd meet me later that evening. Being clueless about me staying there a couple of months, I let him waffle on with directions to the gaff and what I had to do at the Social. Only interested in getting dough into his greedy hands, he ended the call saying I sounded like a Scouser and he already had a Liverpool fella living in one of the flats so I'd feel right at home. Replacing the receiver, I wondered if he'd have felt right at home living with the three jocks downstairs in one of his stinking Chicken Coops. Midday, finished with the social and with the sun high in a turquoise sky, I told Paddy, 'Don't fancy work one iota. We'll leave it till tomorrow and have trip up to the West-End, ay?'

'Don't see why not. Brumbleballs is the boss and he said it'd be okay to do whatever today. Anyway, I'm in need of a little respite and some sightseeing. Brother, you hearing me?'

'Brother, I'm a hearing you loud and clear. Let's be on one!'

'Wharrabout the payout from Vinny though Mickey?'

'Brother, you worry too much. We'll go back about half four. Vinny and tatty Head'll still be there. Come on, you up for it or what?"

'Too right Brother Mickey!'

'How's a walk down the old Kings Road sound Patrick?'

'Fine by me Mickey baby!'

Those little boxes of optimism we'd lifted from the lorry had us role playing two fugitives from an old Starsky and Hutch movie. Checking spirits, the boxes hadn't been the only thing lifted...

7

LEARNING TO FLY

Not wanting to make a big deal of the quick money we'd earned, I still wanted to take a stroll to let the £800 drop into the scheme of things. The hot weather, making it difficult to burrow underground, meant we carried on past Shoreditch tube station to walk up Bethnal Green Road. Here we finally caught a one-stop, Central line tube over to Mile End; then a District Line tube for a several stop journey that ended with us bounding up the escalator two steps at a time at destination Sloan Square. Eager for sunlight, standing at the beginning of Kings Road, we viewed the scenery. Taking in the traffics din, we clocked the passing throng, including hundreds of shitty-arsed pigeons that surrounded the little rectangular Venus Fountain. With shops and buildings combined, here stood the painted landscape known as Sloane Square.

Surroundings checked, we paused to draw a deep breath of clammy, London air. Here, I'm sure we sucked in the floating spirits of the James brothers – like Frank and Jesse had dismounted the tube to go on a robbing spree. Entering the first clothes shop we came upon, with nothing more than a nod of the head, within a three hour period we proceeded to pilfer from shop after shop, and every item of clothing the eyes found pleasurable. Top of the Hoisting hit list: anything labelled with a ridiculously expensive price tag. It was the 'working class kids on a day out routine', when a charrabang full of kids from a council estate go to the zoo and before the teachers can get a grip, all the sweets, drinks and rubber Snakes have wriggled their way out the souvenir shop. Meanwhile, the till drawer remains shut as the Queens purse.

Nothing premeditated happened. We didn't plan it; we didn't talk about it; we just did it. Five or six shops up, we entered this fashion victim shop out of curiosity, with the window display being so bizarre. One of those places that sells £50 ripped tee-shirts and £80 ripped railway workers jeans to people who think it's dead cool to try and look like a dish-cloth. Full of Vivian Westwood type rags and other dishcloth designers, whatever you say about those tatty-tog creators they're all digitally-tuned to the fact that there's always someone out there with more money than sense; someone willing to batter-down those El-bizarro shop doorways with a big wad of cash, while striving to become the new 'ace-face' of the London dishcloth scene.

We hoped Vinny, *the* Alf Ramsey of Canning Town, didn't have just the boys of 66 on his books, and younger punters could be found to buy the dishcloths we'd just left El-bizarro's with. Walking out with garments shoved under armpits, our thin summery jackets slung over one shoulder hid the gear underneath. An obvious ruse, but a mixture of desperateness, good fortune and shopkeepers not noticing the obvious on a warm, sunny day, meant we were lucky enough not to be collared and cuffed. Opportunist thievery they call it: a spontaneous act brought on by the thought of a fast buck – like the eight hundred nicker Vinny promised us this morning!

We couldn't believe the designer price tags being bandied about Kings Road. Clocking the lavish labels made our fingers so itchy they couldn't resist or keep still. Some previous petty thievery, had now, on a warm sunny day in High fashion Street, turned into a kleptomaniac's house warming party at the old Antique Mansion.

By the third or fourth lift, the large, string-handled, carrier bags we'd swiped first port' o' call started overflowing. Sometimes it could be more difficult to swipe a carrier bag than the merchandise on offer. If you asked for one in London, most shop-staff politely told you to fuck-off, unless you genuinely spent Billy Brewster's that is. We'd sussed the carrier bag clause on earlier evening forays into London's bright lights. A lot of shops insisted you to pay for one, or they'd throw-a-blag they were running low and couldn't afford to give them away. Leaving the shop, we'd go, 'You what? The money you'ze make and yer' can't give us a bag!' or the plain English of, 'You lying mingebags!' It was early doors naivety on our part. A real shoplifting firm would never upset shop-staff, let alone bother with carrier bags.

Halfway up Kings Road we came to Chelsea Art College. Sauntering into its gardens, Paddy ushered me in. 'Here, this'll do.'

Stuffing the swagbags deep into a heavily leafed bush, another tasty designer shop showed nearby the art college. With security tags few and far between, we waltzed out with ten pairs of trousers; not dissimilar to the earlier flat-packed, off-the-back-of-a-lorry items. Bouncing around the shops like a couple of honed in missiles, we totally ignored the world revolving around our mission. Making our way back into the college grounds the two missiles landed smack-bang on terra firma. Two Bizzies escorting a drunk from the grounds gave us a serious once-over. The minute they passed, finger-clicked from hypnotism, I motioned, 'Officer Dibble, on the beat, time to leave the street. Departure time...agreed?'

'What's with all the poetry? Ya weirdo! One question about the coats-over-the-shoulder malarkey and it's back of the van for us; come on, *I agree*, let's do one!'

When Paddy asked about the poetry I muttered something about keeping cool – keeping things short and sweet. Maybe because we dressed in building site mode we were luckily ignored. Personally, I knew we stood out like Barney the Dinosaur trying to steal a raincoat from Marks and Sparks but, with wages-gone-a-missing, the two of us seemed unhurried and unworried about the thought of being clapped in irons; well…less than normally. Getting sensible, we left the college grounds piled up with clobber and jumped the first Taxi.

'Drop us at the next tube station along the road please mate.'

'Well, I can take you down to Sloane Square or up the road to Fulham Broadway. It's up to you?'

'Fulham Broadway mate.'

London cabbies, notorious for taking you halfway around the World if you acted and talked tourist, got me acting and talking local. No need in the building togs, I suppose. Leaving the cab we paid a tube fare for the first time ever. Paddy, stumping-up the dough, said. 'No wonder we bunk the fucken' things.'

We looked strange dressed in work clothes weighed down with shopping bags. Paddy had rammed all his swag into carrier bags. I still had five pair of pants wrapped inside my jacket. We joined the exit queue in an orderly fashion and handed our tickets to the guard we normally waltzed past each day. Vinny, at site entrance, was busy guiding a delivery wagon through the narrow gate. Sussing our demeanour and baggage, he ushered us to the hut. 'What've you boys been up to now? Fack me; you don't let the grass grow under yer' feet for long, do ya?'

As he spoke we spilled gear onto the table site joiners had nailed together.

'You'ze two back in work now or you back on the Hoist?'

It was the first time I'd heard the word used in that context. 'On the Hoist, never heard it called that before Vinny?'

'Yer' know it takes time for things to filter up north. Anyway, what've we got' ere then? Fack me, the two lifting Labourer's back on the boil, eh.'

With Vinny speaking the lingo, Paddy asked how old he was.

'Fifty Four I am. What's that got to do with it?'

'Well, yer' don't get many streetwise oul' fellers; if yer' get me drift?'

'Listen son, my parents came here from Cork in Southern Ireland. I was born in Canning Town. I've travelled over t'see relations a few times and I've been to Liverpool on the odd occasion as well. London, Cork, Liverpool; these places are not as different as you think. I did my Army with Scouser's, Glaswegian's, and Londoner's and we could normally find a common bond. Yeah, when I was your age I thought Londoner's were the bees-knees, yer' know, the only wiseguys if you like, but that notion took a kick in the teeth in my early army days once I met a few conniving Scousers. I mean, if I was such a fackin' wiseguy, I wouldn't be on a building site at fifty-four years of bleeding age would I. Don't let my age fool yer'. I've been getting up to all sorts of nonsense all me life t'get by. Things ain't gonna change now. Yer' see son, putting it mildly, I was having a fackin' good dance long before you were born!'

Vinny speaking our language, albeit with a strong Cockney twang, meant that day onward we got on superbly. Paddy, never one for hard labour, started shooting to Vinny's hut every hour or so for a giggle and a cuppa. He got on with him better than anyone on site. Vinny mentioned that Paddy reminded him of himself when he was younger. Viewing the assembled threads heaped about the makeshift table, he widened his eyes at the colourfully loud, dishcloth collection.

'Yer' see the fackin' prices on these string vests? I don't know if I can do them for full-whack. We'll see tonight. Not in any rush for the money are yer' Mickey?'

'Nah, get what yer' can for the poncey, fashion stuff. Can yer' still get us a third on the formal gear though?'

'Yeah, should be no problem. Anyway, I've got a nice surprise for you two.'

Reaching into his blue overall, he found the hip pocket. Nestled inside was a sweet little wad of Queen Lizzie's. He handed the wad to me. 'There you go boys, eight hundred nicker; how'ze that?'

'Fucksake Vinny, *We* don't let the grass grow. That was a bit quick!'

'Look, anything you'ze get, bring to me. I'll always find a buyer.'

I turned to Paddy. 'We'll have to be careful here kiddo, the sideline could end up outstripping the main job.'

"Nah…we won't have the time, and it won't fall off the back of a lorry everyday.'

'Maybe not, but we're in London now, and this place is like twenty town centre's stuck together; there's thousands of shelves it can fall off!'

I wasn't being a smart-arse, it's just the money had come easy compared to digging trenches all day. With my recent history I wasn't dismissing any opportunity lightly. Speaking in length to Vinny, our new Site Foreman, he explained a long lunch-hour might be the way forward with our new enterprise. Paddy had his doubts. 'It's not long though is it, Vinny? I mean, an hour to cop for some gear. We'd end up coming back with bits: socks and undies and shit!'

'Point taken; anyway, I shouldn't be encouraging you. The Old Bill will have you listening to this summers' World Cup on radios in the Scrubs if you're not facken' careful!'

'We'll be alright. You'll see; nothing heavy; just a few quid now and again.'

Part youthful bravado, part wanting more money, Paddy and I didn't need much encouragement once we'd crossed the Hoisting line. Fast cash had rolled in and, like catch of the day, we were truly hooked. Paddy, already acting the playboy on labourers bunce, constantly lavishing dough on new conquests, was reeled-in easy as me. The only time he'd stay in was when two girls got wind of his philandering ways, kerboshing his shagging plans last minute. Going on a double date with him, he'd wind Boney up, shouting, 'I'm meeting a little darling who'd love a bite of your Swiss roll, Anthony.' While with me, it was a purely case of wanting to return home one day and tell my Ma and Da that, 'Hey! I don't need their shitty handouts or their shitty jobs; they can shove it up their pinstriped arseholes! I've got me own dough and me own thing going on.' In truth, I thought Liverpool and the North had been shit on, and I didn't care if I shat somewhere else!

Meantime, Boney jibbed the one night a week acting classes, saying it was full of wannabe Shakespeare's and Laurence Olivier's' and he couldn't read or understand some of the pieces they presented to him. Full of the 'Macbeth mob' and not enough 'Italian Jobs' he told us. Bottom line: you couldn't get him out the bookies. If you did, it'd be, 'Who fancies shooting over to Madame Persia's or Madame Claudine's for a Coppers Cosh.'

Although it could take over an hour to get to the brass yards of Soho from the Chicken Coops of Illford, made no difference to him; he'd found *woman!* And, even if they were the women of Soho with their baggy worn out pussies, they were still gonna get his wages – yeah – right between the lips!

Being surrounded by the Warren Beatty of Illford's small nightclub scene, and Boney, the prostitutes and bookies surefire banker, I tried acting the finance guru again. I knew instantly that the lifting-lark had no long term legs for those two, and one day soon Officer Dibble was gonna come-a-calling, but, try as I might, Monday morning I'd be lending them tens and twenties all over again.

It became a Monday morning ritual at ten o'clock tea-break to deposit whatever I had over from the weekend into my account at Barclays. For psychological reasons, I called it my Big Time Charlie account, and with financial advice again falling on deaf ears, I'd be permanently lending money out to the two of them, complicating saving plans I had of my own.

Thinking how I could get them to open a bank account, I offered. 'Come the day I'm a Big Time Charlie, when the account bears fruit, you'ze two will still be digging holes in the London soil. Meanwhile, I'll be having tea at the Dorchester with the ghost of Keith Moon and his floating drum kit.'

'What the fuck're you on about now? The day I win the big one yer' won't be saying that. And what's with Keith Moon anyway?' Boney enquired.

'Big one! As if…yer' dope! Keith Moon's the only fella I can think of who could twat yer' hard enough with his drumsticks to maybe knock some sense into yer' about yer' stupid horse racing ideas!'

'But Keith Moons long dead.'

'Yeah, and so will I be before you win any big fucken' race, Dickhead!'

Paddy laughed. 'Yeah, maybe Mickey, but while you're having tea in the lobby, I'll be in the basement nightclub dancing with Sam Fox and Fiona Fullerton.'

I Sniggered. 'Those two Tory bitches wouldn't give you the time of day once they sussed the two brass meg's you carry round in yer' back bin.'

The joke seemed to hit home and the two of them opened savings accounts at the same Barclays Bank. It was still a complete waste of bank paper. In all the time they were open they didn't deposit a flimsy, yellow Monopoly nicker into either stash!

We'd got a nice weekly rhythm on the go: the usual Fri/Sat bender, followed by a Sunday afternoon of rest and recovery. Monday to Friday, into work, and the long lunch-hour Vinny talked about, we spent Hoisting clobber in the surrounding designer and formal wear shops; usually chain-store branches like Next and Austin Reed. Saturday meant shop graft, with the days Hoisting hours being determined by whether we did overtime that morning. Come Monday – lifting payday – we'd be in line for good bung on top of our honest-to-god wages.

Vinny, regular as clockwork with payment, meant the small amount of goods and clothing we lifted each day, turned large amount in the pound note stakes come Saturday afternoon.

Crooked wages started to outstrip straight wages, which remained three hundred pounds a week. Like the rest of the Yuppies in the city, I started using a filofax to keep up – funny – Ha, tell me about it! Maybe the only person using one for shoplifting purposes in the whole area? Earning eight to nine hundred pounds a week, in the 1980's, for us, was the monetary equivalent of paying a Russian street urchin the same or more today. At times it felt like we were three of Boney's imaginary Cockneys, who all had money falling out of their arse pockets!

Keeping clean formal clothes inside Vinny's hut, we'd quickly change into Yuppie togs and persona before lunch; then, back into work clothes end of lunch. Dreading heavy rain – getting changed with mud about was a pain – we became as adept at changing as theatre actors backstage. Boney, weekday 'bagman', normally kept lookout across the street from any place we entered. Abnormally was nearer the truth. We didn't trust him inside the shop, but he'd have the odd mooch among the racks on weekend excursions into the outlying suburbs. Boney having a mooch often led to some kind of close-call. Limiting him to suburb Hoisting, due to easier pilfering outside London, I told Paddy. 'Further afield we go, easier things get. But, with Boney wanting a go, further we travel, further we get into trouble!'

Merchandise lifted, we'd dispatch direct to the bagman so we didn't have the Kings Road problem of traipsing about with carrier bags, or looking for hiding places to stash swag. Vinny, true to his word, kept coming up with the readies'. Sometimes we couldn't supply him quick enough. Workers on site started putting orders in and, as it was no use trying to hide what we were upto, a few, slightly envious by nature, were given good deals to get into the swing of things. We continually assessed workers on site; watching for any shifty, undercover plod tendencies. Vinny, the main protector of our livelihood gently let a few people know what could happen to them if they were sussed as on-site grasses. We didn't need bricklaying Bizzies on this site. Some of the rag-arsed Cockney bandit's who paid him a visit left you in no doubt about his acquaintances. His two sons alone looked like beefed-up Mitchell brothers long before the East end brothers were scripted.

Even the dwellers of McRents Chicken Coops – once they picked their Dole cheques up – started buying stuff. In the Ultravox Jocks case: when their cravats had too many baked bean stains, and their Hitler macs started looking like they'd been rolling around in festival mud at Woodstock for a week. Any Hoisting coats, looking tatty on the graft, got hastily retired to the Jocks wardrobe. The keyboard crew ended up with more coats than a wooden house on the white cliffs of Dover.

My newly occupied Chicken Coop, full of gadgets and strange items of clothing that Vinny, try as he might, could not find a buyer for, became seriously cramped. Small bed apart, the room had reverted back to its original use as a walk-in-wardrobe. We even kept some of the other tenants sweet, as they'd often catch us coming into McRents laden down with Saturday's takings. Terry the Manc was all right, same for the Scottish keyboard firm, but not knowing Clifford and Barry White too well we'd take them little parcels of food and the odd tee-shirt. It cheered them up no end. It was a buzz to see their faces light up from the giving of a mere morsel – bedsit life, ay!

Paddy, favouring one of those green-waxed Barbour coats – no longer the sole preserve of land-owning country folk and the Tory hunting fraternity – blended in perfectly with Yuppie bankers and stockbrokers frequenting the Holborn and City Of London area. Spending most of our long lunch-break in and around this vicinity, we sometimes jumped a bus down the Holborn High Road, reaching as far as St. Giles in the West or

Whitechapel and Spitalfields in the East. As weeks flew we picked-up most of the tricks involved in the Hoisting trade and started using shoplifting slang and lifting lingo everyday of the week. Other sites nearby started barricading their entry points as plant hire carried on going AWOL at an alarming rate. When builders from other sites mentioned 'shrinkage' we just agreed that we had the same problem. Machinery from other sites was a great weekend side-liner. Often a master key, or a key taken off site after one of us had mingled with the construction site workers was all we needed.

Boney and I started wearing long summer raincoats, specially adapted by a tailor friend of Vinny's up in Canning Town. He'd sewn pockets as big as pillowcases inside the lining from waist down. So, instead of taking one or two shirts, the onus was on taking three or four...or five. Busy on the Hoist, I'd look out the shop window and spy Boney across the road trying to act the office worker. I'd nudge Paddy in Boney's direction; ending with us having to leave the premises in fits.

Most early lifting days we spent concocting new ideas to get gear out of the shop. One Monday morning, on the tube to work, I noticed this plain Jane kind of girl about twenty years of age staring over. She looked like Lisa Tarbuck: dark hair, slightly overweight, only wearing glasses. Turning, I noticed a bored Paddy giving her the eye, with her returning coy little smiles. Watching the tube version of Blind Date, Boney's got his head buried in the racing pages, oblivious as usual. Going on for a few stops, I smiled at Paddy. 'Don't you ever give up?'

'Say fuck all Mickey; she's the bird who works in that designer shop near Petticoat Lane.'

A couple of stops up, a seat emptied next to the girl. Paddy waltzed over. Within the next four weeks she must have supplied us with fifty John Smedley lambswool tops. These lovely, buttoned-up sweaters retailed at around fifty Quid, and Vinny would get us a third, or just over a third. Fifty times eighteen was decent dosh over a four-week period. John Smedley tops, being very popular at the time, bit like Fred Perry's in the late seventies, meant we couldn't get enough of them. Entering once a week, usually around lunchtime, there would be one other staff member knocking about the shop. Getting Ann-Maries attention from outside, so she knew we were coming in, meant she'd make a beeline to serve us before anybody else could.

It became a little obvious after a while, so we started to buy the odd pair of socks, but even the 'small-buy ruse' wore a bit thin. Eventually, like other shops we visited too frequently, we stopped going altogether. It was always hard to pull yourself away from such an obvious earner. Paddy carried on seeing Ann-Marie for a while, even though our lunch-hour visits stopped. He told us about her being a danger woman on the nest (never judge a book by the cover) and she'd apparently showed the Illford Stud a thing or two between the sheets. For that reason, he didn't find it easy to stop seeing her…bit like me with the shop come to think of it.

Ann-Marie, from Leytonstone, paid Paddy a visit at McRents on the odd occasion. One night he knocked at the door of my Chicken Coop in a bedraggled state. 'Listen, this nympho wants two's up. She's been on at me for weeks, and I promised her I'd do the honours. Who fancies it?'

Boney shot out of his door quicker than the motorized rabbit on a greyhound track. 'Me, I'll do the biz. Come on Mickey, she's a tidy bird that Ann-Marie, I wouldn't mind some of that. You don't mind stepping down do yer'?'

It simply wasn't happening for me with mates present. I mean, if you fancy a woman, who wants to see some fellers skid-marked underpants lying on the bedroom floor, or a pair of spiky red onions that have just left those undies behind pummelling away the minute they touch fresh-air? 'Yeah, no problem Boney lad. Nice to see you so quick on the uptake. Go on stallion, give Ann-Marie one for me!'

Being honest, I became intrigued to see her reaction to Boneys King Edward cigar. At one point, tempted to have a listen at the door, I realised anyone coming out onto the landing, especially Miserable Tits, would have all the ammo in the world for labelling me McRent's top perve. From the landing you could hear laughing, followed by shuffling about as they manoeuvred for position. I went back to my new telly, trying to forget about the live porn scene down the corridor. Paddy opened the door ten minutes later. I tried to act disinterested. Noticing this, he played hard to get…I caved-in first. 'Fuck it! Okay, I'm sussed. Get on with it.'

'I've left Boney in there with nympho knickers. That's the first woman I've met who's worse than a man. We only lasted five minutes. Once we'd stopped, Ann-Marie took one look at Boney's Swiss-roll, looks me up and down and goes: 'Makes yours look like a Dunlop tyre-valve doesn't it' Cheeky cow!'

Laughing out loud, Boney and Ann-Marie came to investigate. Walking funny, she set me off again. Bedsit doors opened and heads appeared. The Keyboard Jocks wandered upstairs as Ultravox music hit the hallway. Clifford was at his door, and Barry White showed face. I think Terry the Salford Jet had flown over the park to get some peace with Bernadette. Thank god Miserable Tits wasn't about. Turning to Ann-Marie, I said. 'Stand still on the landing Ann-Marie, let's see if I can push a chest of drawers through yer' legs?

Paddy and I were in bulk. Even though what I'd said had been extremely rude, Ann-Marie, laughing herself, said to Paddy, 'Hey, Jelly Baby, don't you laugh!' Then to me, 'And as for you shy boy, let's see what you've got to hide. If yer' gobs anything to go by, it should be massive.

With the onus on me, the laughing subsided. 'Fuck that Ann-Marie; I'm not getting me todger out for anybody!'

'Come on big-licks, you've had yer' laugh; now's my turn. Get them off!'

'Nah, no way; no one's interested.'

'I'm interested. All mouth and no trousers ay Mickey, don't you reckon fellers?'

She'd turned things full-circle. Paddy, Boney and the others joined in.

'Yeah, come on Mickey, get them off! You heard the lady!'

'Alright, alright Ann-Marie, point taken; but I'm deffo not dropping me kecks, especially here on the landing!'

Once the other tenants dispersed back to their rooms, I thought: *he's right, she is worse than a fella*. Being something of a wild woman and such a laugh we wanted to take her out for a night on the town. Plus, though we'd given her a decent dropsy for the Smedley earners, she deserved more with the money she'd made us. Although some fellers don't take kindly to a mouthy woman, we took her out, she copped for a local stallion wearing gear we knew had come from us, and everyone was happy. Earning well and being new to the East End, we didn't need to upset our new applecart. Noticing Ann Marie eyeing him, while with us, the sharply-dressed stallion, hoping for a treat, eyed us warily. Eventually making his move, all he got was good luck and best wishes.

Having a drink with Vinny in Canning Town, Bethnal Green and Stratford, he'd be quietly pointing out feller's wearing our swag. Sometimes half the boozer seemed to be dressed in knock-off clobber. There's me in Liverpool thinking where I lived was Black Market Central, with everyone round the country paying top-whack, and all the time these Londoners have got the best of both worlds: all the jobs, dosh and prospects, plus a black market economy just as expansive as the one on the banks of the Mersey. Mentioning Ann-Marie to Vinny, he said. 'Listen boys, I'm not jealous. My wife's forty-eight and she's got something in her knickers that no girl of Ann-Marie's age could ever have.'

Clocking each other, amused, Paddy asked. 'Oh yeah, what's that then Vinny?'

'It's her tit's innit!'

He introduced us to characters like Billy Birdsegg: named because he frequented the Essex countryside on bird's egg finding missions. Four foot ten with a face like a squashed Rod Stewart, Billy was just as mean with his dosh as the ol' plastic Jock was said to be himself. Out and about in our round of drinks, we found he was forty years of age, a father of four miniature Billy's and one narky little bastard to boot!

A night on the town with Billy always involved a clash with a stranger…or friend. Billy would fight anyone. Linger too long on the Ronnie Corbett statistics, take the Michael out of his ornithological hobby, his tightly zipped pockets or his streaky bacon hairdo, and it was going off big time. Most confrontations, surprisingly, began with those immortal words of snarl: 'Who the fuck are you looking at?' Seeing as most people naturally looked straight over his head?

Disappearing, unsurprisingly, when it was his round one evening, Vinny informed us Birdsegg was so tight he'd been the first fella round their manor to get double-glazing. We looked on confused? Till Paddy asked, 'Oh I see Vinn, yer' mean so he could save a few bob on heating bills?'

'Nah, fack that Paddy; he got the double-glazing installed so his kids couldn't hear the ice-cream van driving round the block!'

Teetering on the brink of stack-heels and violence, he kicked-off three times within the space of a weekend one time. Wondering how many times Birdsegg had turned the battle lights on throughout his life, it wouldn't surprise me if Billy was *lights-out* by now. Strange how lots of titchy fellers have volcanic tempers bubbling away inside those squashed little bonces. Trying to prove something, I suppose. Watch out, watch out, there's a midget about!

Boney had been an avid egg-collector, and one Saturday morning at Browns department store in South Molton Street he came on top Hoisting expensive shirts and ended up doing a runner into Bond Street tube station. Commenting, I said, 'Ay

Boney, you and that Birdsegg don't half rattle on about collecting eggs. I bet the poor birds were on you the minute you went to lift eggs from the nest.'

'Oh yeah, why's that?'

'Stands to reason, I mean, every time you lift a few shirts from the shelf, shop staff are on you straight away.'

Bombing back in the taxi to Illford, Paddy laughed. 'Yeah Boney, how come every time we come on top it's down to you, dickhead? From now on stick to bagman like you started out.'

I agreed, 'It's alright if a Kestrel swoops on yer' curly wig, but it's not alright if you get swooped on by Floorwalkers or Bizzies and we end up in jug.'

Though mocking in jest, I'd confided in Paddy that the first major mistake to lead us to jail would deffo be down to Boney. The law of shoplifting averages was bound to intervene, and Boney, our rusty cog in the chain, needed a lot more than a tweak of WD40 to loosen then tighten *his* lifting technique. Nerve-jangling trips apart, he'd also been gabbing about earners on site. We reprimanded him about loose lips and the damage it could do to earning potential and livelihoods. We'd left Liverpool skint, jobless, with no prospects, with hardly anybody below us on the UK food chain. Though we scurried around London's underbelly trying to earn a crust, I'd become more determined than ever not to return to Liverpool's with mine empty.

Another fella Vinny introduced was Marty Cakemix; so called because he'd trained as a Chef on a Royal Navy vessel. Leaving the Navy he'd married a Wren he'd met while stationed abroad. When I said to Birdsegg he too should have married a Wren – in the feathered tense – he fixed me with the dreaded glare. 'What d'you mean by that then, Scouse? You taking the piss or what? Is it because it's a tiny little bird? Is that what you mean?'

'Whoa, whoa there tiger!' Interrupting the narky little bastard, I explained with him loving all things birdlike, a Wren was a bird, in the feathered tense, not the tiny tense. Adding that, maybe Boney could marry a pretty Flamingo, or a golden Goose, or even an Ostrich wearing a pair of suspenders for that matter! I continued, 'so you could have married a lovely litt…err…gorgeous Wren.'

'Oh! I see…but a Wren is one of the smallest birds isn't it?'

Vinny butted in. 'Shut the fuck up Billy! The lads not having a pop; he's just making conversation. Ok!' Only Vinny had a way with Billy.

Cakemix, a Chef of some distinction, got his name from a story that he'd supposedly baked a cake to poison and kill his nagging, little, Wren-of-a-wife; leaving Marty to pick up the insurance money and a suspicious story that wouldn't go away. We told Vinny it was all half-baked, and she'd probably choked on his bad breath. Calling us over, Cakemix would ask what we were drinking. A good spender and good company for travelling stories, he told us all about life on the seven seas and the scrapes he got into from Tottenham to Torremolinos.

Going on one night, he mentioned a couple of his bell-bottomed-buddies came from Liverpool and he'd docked there on a few occasions, only to be mugged one time after leaving the notorious Grafton nightclub. Apparently this gorgeous young dolly had been giving him the fluttery eyelids. So, come two o'clock, he thought Christmas had come early when the Sophia Loren lookalike told him she lived in Kensington, a tough Liverpool district half a mile from the club. Believe me, this Kensington was down to earth, bears-arse to phoney, silk bum-cheek compared to the posh London area bordering Hyde Park. A taxi wouldn't be necessary she told him, as he walked her home. Cakemix said he sobered-up quickly once the wind whipped up from the Mersey shoreline. He couldn't wait to get back to Sophia's Kensington terrace to unwrap his early Chrimbo gift. The last thing he remembered was a sign saying Pythian Street, then sweet dreams baby…

Waking up at the Royal Liverpool Hospital, the nurse told him he'd been found minus his shirt and pants, with the words 'Sailor for sale' written across his belly in black mascara. He reckoned they'd removed his spray-on pants because they were so tight you'd have needed a tin opener to extract the hefty wedge lodged inside his hip pocket. Putting 'Sailor for sale' across his belly let him know the Scouse Sophia Loren had set him up, as he couldn't remember letting anyone else know he was a ships chef on shore leave – tongue twister of a mugging or what!

He later found it was definitely Pythian Street where he'd been waylaid after he visited a solicitor about a criminal injuries claim – adding nicely to his recent insurance pay off. He said he bore no grudges against our little firm, or our Northern clan; but, that was part of his slyness. Constantly trying to get us to sell him gear direct, not through Vinny, this shady Sailor could spin a yarn and wind you in, before springing the main question. 'Alright Mickey, come on, I'm paying top dollar for my rig-outs; what about getting me some nice strides and dickie dirt's to sell meself. I'll pay above whatever your normal fence pays.'

He knew who we sold it through. In his own snidey way he wouldn't say his name. We never told Vinny. He'd have knocked seven kinds of shite out of the slippery Sailor. Again, we didn't need to upset the status quo on our new paying manor. Soon as Cakemix told me he'd been necking the lips off a Sophia Loren lookalike I had him down as a truth stretcher. Face like the Singing Detective apart, his breath blew garlic sausage covered in dog shit, and with sugar puff teeth like that Shane McGowan lookalike, it had to be a set-up. No Grafton dolly bird would have gone near his blotchy red kipper with honest intent; especially as it spewed week-old cabbage in a pan whenever he spun a yarn.

With ol' Vinny knocking the clobber out in fine style, I rapidly built a tidy wedge in my Big time Charlie account. Only blip on the horizon: Paddy and Boney, my Friday-loaded, Monday-skint shipmates, who showed no signs of putting any Pillsbury dough aside for the obvious rainy day. The heavens, bound to open the moment we were clapped in irons, equalled no dough-on-show and even more rainy days, as playing catch-up we'd be bang on the Hoist till the Bizzies bracelets found their way to our wrists, again, and again, and again.

During the hot summer days of 86, the Mexico World Cup, after a wonderful opening ceremony, bounced along. England stood a good chance of making it to the Final, with the only things ominous: the searing Mexican heat and the fact they didn't have a Maradona. Maybe John Barnes on his day, but he never really produced his best at international level. We thought England should play Peter Beardsley in every game, as his smile could frighten everybody off the pitch, leaving England to pick up the cup!

Job-wise, we were ship-shape, with building work and Hoisting days intertwining like one occupation. When things slackened on-site Vinny made sure it wasn't the labourers who got the first kick up the arse like they usually did. To make it difficult for Brumble to get rid of us, we started having a go at the odd trade job on site. Painting became mainly our responsibility, saving Brumble from employing time-served tradesman. Although involved in hod-carrying and the odd bit of plumbing and joinery, Vinny told Boney to stay away from the painting, as applying a fresh coat to new red brick along with windows and frames wasn't the idea.

Frequenting the West End more often, department stores off Regent, Oxford and Carnaby Street, like Lilywhites, Selfridges, and Marks and Sparks, got regular visits for refunding purposes. Anything taken from Marksy's could be taken back to any of their stores for a cash refund, so M&S refund routes were put in place. Socialising – if you could call it that – meant the odd visit to Madame Claudine's for a brass polish. With the money those Soho strumpets made, I wondered why the curtains were more tattered than the ones at McRents. Surely those ladies of the night – and day – could afford some decent drapes to keep the sun from shining on the punters ring-pieces. With the hours they put in, they probably ended up with pussies as wide as the Mersey Tunnel; a gap only their own stuffed purses could fill. Soho ladies of the night – Ha! Don't make me laugh! More like ladies of the fucking permanent shift!

Boney, a season ticket holder and twice weekly visitor to Madame Claudine's would have us waiting inside one of those coffee shops that abounded Soho's streets. Sometimes, tired of hanging about, we'd venture upstairs through boredom more than necessity. It felt strange: one moment Hoisting clobber from a West End designer shop, fifteen minutes later, lying on top of Miss Lulu doing you're sweaty press-ups – all the time checking over her shoulder for the swagbag you'd stuffed under the window chair. Boney, normally shy with women, paid-up for lost time. With no conversational skills required for this type of fornication, it was a reasonable transaction for both parties. The Prozzies: they got paid, and Boney: he got some well needed practice in.

With the amount of female company Paddy was keeping he had no need to indulge. While, fussy as usual, I never liked the thought of some Turkish wrestler's walnuts resting in exactly the same place as mine only fifteen minutes previous. Once Boney boredom set-in and we ventured upstairs to pay for it, I'd get this empty feeling when finished – not in the testicular sense – I mean, unfulfilling, with a woman probably going through the motions for the seventh or eighth time that day. Looking directly into her eyes I'd see no turned-on, loving emotion whatsoever. Sometimes a little pain lying deep in her psyche would reveal itself for a passing moment; guaranteed to make me lose a hard on. I'd end up fantasising about some gorgeous past conquest to get the job done, while she gave me the, '*come on, time is money*' look that made me regret coming in in the first place.

Crack-riddled, drug-driven variety apart, I struggled to understand the bravery, desperateness or need of a woman who sold herself this way. Easy money – don't think so! The odd, clean, decent looking, storefront dummy, followed by two fat, overweight, BO perfumed, articulated lorry drivers; then, cup of tea and quick fanny rinse for lunch, followed by two Muslim onion chomper's just waltzed off a long-haul flight from Calcutta; finishing the earning day, with two Jamaican Yardies, one of whom has got a knob like Boney and it feels like its pushing up your ribs, and the other who's been wearing the same stinking, worn-out undergarments for the past three months. Nah, not for me sir! A strong, abandoned, yet, couldn't-give-a-shit kind of woman indeed!

A whole new landscape presented itself to us, and money, like a surging tributary breaking free from the main stream, started flowing towards normally dull and lifeless pockets. Some old mates back home, hearing about our good fortune – or whatever you want to call it – got the idea it might be the opportunity *they* were looking for. I knew one more scallywag meant seven or eight more scallywags. I told Paddy and, especially Boney, to keep schtum about extra income we'd been earning, and any probing questions from the Fatherland needed to be blanked. No work on site and no room at McRents became the word. I felt like relenting by bringing one of mine or Paddy's brothers into the frame, but I knew it would only curtail the life expectancy of what we'd got up and running.

Though tempted to tell people back home we were doing well, the silencers were on. We told friends and relations we lived in a shoebox, which we did, and lived lives of typical migrant workers: shitty living conditions, average wages that didn't go far in expensive London, and missing home and family everyday. Having no pride in the fact we spent most of our free time bang on the Hoist, we knew most lads wouldn't last a week living the bedsit life and were bound to run home screaming highway robbery stories. Lip-zipped was the best policy. London life had opened up for us, and opened our eyes. Suddenly, two hundred miles down the road, we had prospects, and a place where you didn't have to live your life as a no-mark dole-ite. No more scraping by on a pittance. Starting to enjoy ourselves it got me thinking: *go with the flow; if it's not broke, why the fuck fix it!*

The Saturday morning after England drew their second World Cup game 0-0 with Morocco, I pinned a huge map of Greater London up on the wall. After some heady pub conversation with Vinny, his sons, Birdsegg and Cakemix, the best shopping/shoplifting towns surrounding London got circled and put on a Hoisting hitlist. Three days earlier Portugal had beaten England one-nil in their opening game of the tournament. For Boney it was looking same old, same old. 'Wharra load of Shite! We'll forget the World Cup for another four years. I should never have put a bet on that bunch of tosser's anyway!' He screamed at the final whistle, lashing another crunched up betting slip through the bedsit window.

McRents now had an original betting slip driveway. Northern Ireland and Scotland both reached the Mexico finals, and the Raincoat/Ultravox Jocks made themselves heard around the Chicken Coops with some noisy vocal support. It made a nice change from the droning keyboard variety.

After paying us from Brumble's float for masonry drills, angle grinders and small plant hire lifted from a nearby tool hire shop – another regular earner – Vinny mentioned there'd be no overtime that weekend. With the Hoisting scene paying so well we smiled at the news. Jokingly, we said he purposely didn't provide us with weekend work as his *other* earnings would take a dip. He went on about the Hoisting game having a brief shelf life and we'd be better concentrating on nine to five. After offering advice he ended up admitting we were a lost cause; his final words: 'I was the same meself; you'ze young buckos will never listen. You're just gonna have to learn the lessons yer' selves.'

Acting the smart-arse, I replied, 'Dead right Vinn; so, come on boys, lets gerrout and learn those lessons!'

Going at it, a full day shopping could bring in as much as a week's wages. With that in mind we set off to Windsor Saturday morning with the reasoning: it sounded posh, we were keen to see Windsor Castle and, apparently the town, always crowded with tourists, meant it got marked-up as 'busier the better' in the lifting ledger.

Bunking a Metropolitan tube to Paddington, we boarded an over ground train to Slough. Changing trains for the short journey to Windsor, I made a mental note we'd had to catch four trains since leaving Gants Hill; far too many for normal graft. With no tickets – stupid, I know – we didn't need to be dodging guards and inspectors half the day. Doubting we'd visit Windsor or its castle again, unless we had wheels, it was time to make the most.

On the mainline train we viewed Eton College and its grounds. The snooty, upper-crust school, to me, remained a whopping big symbol of the British Class system. Throwing a forlorn two fingers up as it passed into the distance, I had to explain to Boney why? – Again, a complete waste of time! Leaving Windsor station, stunned by the sheer scale of the castle, we realized it dwarfed and dominated the small town. Paddy, noting the grandeur of the place, quipped, 'So this is just one of the Queens retreats is it; not much in common with a caravan in North Wales is it!'

Paddy and I, still slightly overwhelmed by the Royal gaff, got our heads turned back to the High Street by an impatient Boney. 'Yeah, it's not a bad castle, but Conway, Caernarfon, Rhyl, they're all the same; just castles aren't they. Come on, here's a designer shop, let's get to it!'

Playfully, I shoulder-charged him aside, 'Boney, slow down brother; remember what we said about being Bagman. Find yourself a nice café to sit and study the form. Talking castles, I'm sure you'd rather check the runners for the 3:15 at Sandcastle.'

Passing him the Daily Mirror, I pointed to the door of the first English brekkie on the road. Blimping inside, I seen Formica, tea-stained tables, crooked chairs, miss-matched cutlery, sauce bottles with blobs of gunge oozing from the tops and the usual lady in waiting: a bearded and overall'ed Dot Cotton. Carrying a spoon in her top pocket and biro behind one ear, she twiddled nervously with a notepad that said park your arse we're ready to rumble. It looked our usual rendezvous in every way, except Windsor's Dot Cotton hadn't had a shave for a week.

'Boney, get yer' arse in gear and tell George Best to get the bangers in the pan. And, don't start opening yer' gob letting half the world know why we're here...Ok! Oh, and by the way, don't get brown sauce all over me paper.'

'Yes yer' honour. Now you two hurry up and fetch some swag for the bag. That new Miss Yvonne's waiting for me at Madame Claudine's in Soho...Don't be long.'

Though he brought a smile to our faces you still had to stress the importance of every little detail to Boney. With Paddy, mutter the briefest and he'd be right to it...

'Paddy, get in here!'

First gaff: run-of-the-mill sports shop. Typical High Street sports stockist meant tracksuits or racquets. We started supplying Vinny, who supplied Brumble, who supplied his court-game bum chums with the most expensive tennis, badminton and squash racquets on offer. Most of these places sold half-decent sports trackies, racquets and footwear, but only top-end sports emporiums like Lilywhites sold designer gear too. Forgetting designer togs and tags for now, we made our way to the tracksuit display hanging in one corner.

Cardboard hoardings advertising Mexico 86 stood about the shop, meaning we had to weave our way through to tracksuit corner. Shop-staff approached asking if we'd like help. Using an American accent, I replied 'No sir, just looking, while our wives and children admire this damn, fine castle of yours.'

Shop-staff: fifty-ish; Eric Morcambe-ish and probably the manager, spoke softly in Queens English. 'Let me know if you need any help.'

About-turning, he returned to emptying stock from new boxes.

Paddy kept Eric in check, repeating, 'Yeah, it's alright – alright – alright – alright – Whoa! A minute, nah – nah – yeah – yeah, go on its Ok. Ok. Ok. Ok. Okay okaaaay.'

I'd rolled two Adidas tracksuits up and slowly placed them into the large inside pocket of my knee length raincoat. You could see a slight swelling in the coat if you looked *real* hard. Small bulge apart, nobody could tell unless they'd seen the gear drop directly into pocket. Lifting ledger: If shop-staff notice anything iffy, never leave the premises till you've taken them back out.

'Paddy, everything custy?'

'Yeah, no problemo; away you go.'

Unless the premises are staff-less, or its owners are day dreaming in retail space, never leave immediately. First: browse, giving your interested shopper impression. Nice smile helps. No screwed-up, robbers dog grimaces. Second: if everything looks hunky dory, with no sussy-bleepers, and your partners giving you the all-clear, then, and only then, you leave. Toddling out to a sunny Saturday morning in Windsor and a town rammed with tourists, we edged across the road. Boney, engrossed in the gee-gee pages didn't notice me enter the café. I smiled at the bearded lady who'd served his sausage sarnie and whipped it from under his nose.

'You'ze were quick; ay, givvus me sarnie back!'

'How come you never ordered us one, tight-arse?'

'Didn't think you'd be so quick. Hang on, I'll order two more.'

'Don't bother Bone, I'll have one when I've switched off. Open the bag.'

Taking a bite from Boney's sarnie, while clocking Dot, I deposited the rolled-up tracksuits into the swagbag between his feet in one movement. Leaving the café, I noticed Paddy giving the recognised whistle down the road. I returned a stop sign with the palm of my hand so he knew he was in view. Once I'd caught up, he offered, 'Not much in the way of shops this yard. I took some racquets from that last gaff. I'm not full, so I won't have to unload. Don't think we'll last long in Lizzie's back garden. I've had a scout around. It's only a few streets big. Come in this place down here; there's some Italian stuff in the window.'

Entering, a bell tinkled. No one appeared on chime. Fast scanning the compact area for prying eyes came back negative – time to be affirmative. Seizing the moment, we fast-binned three pair of Zegna pants each; patting them down till they lodged tightly within our coats. Making sure there were no gaps on the rail, we pushed the other pants together. Still no one appeared. With a no-show you'd start thinking all kinds: shop-staff had a secret hole in the wall; they'd disguised themselves as dummies; they peeped between coat hangers. It was *the* old suspicious nature in over-drive; paranoid on an easy lift, paranoid when not. They'd normally be upstairs or in a back office, or be gambling on no custom by shooting out for a quick sarnie, a natter or a visit to the bogs. All equated to loss of earnings if you were dithery of foot.

'What d'yer' reckon sir, another fill, or time to depart?' I asked.

'Fill her up Jacko! Those Daniel Hechter shirts, same number again.'

Shirts swallowed, we left the gaff. The bell chimed twice as loud now we'd loaded. Still nobody showed face. I looked at the phoney Italian sign above the door – one of those stupid Italiano Cooliano names they have to make a gaff sound high class. Tempted to dart back inside, I dithered a little. Paddy, reading the look, reeled me in, 'Time to do one; enough's enough. Come on, we've just got here.'

Back at the Bearded Lady's I told Boney to order the sausage sarnies. Scooping the blue Adidas bag from under the table, I headed for the basement toilet. Paddy gave the lady a wink then followed. Stuffing gear into the bag, I hung around for thirty seconds before accompanying Paddy back to the seats. Upstairs, the delicious smell of frying bacon greeted our reappearance. The Tourists had eaten all the bangers. 'They always want to try English sausages', she explained, her spikey top lip momentarily putting me off my food.

I thought about whether *we* were tourists or not…tea-leaf tourists…minor details? The lady, more cotton-chinned than Dot Cotton, brought two more cups of tea for Boney and Paddy, a large glass of milk for me and two fat bacon sarnies. Amid eager taste buds, with Dot out of view, I spoke mid-bite. 'Boney, don't stray to the betting office. Don't think we'll last long in Windsor. Sit tight till we finish these. We'll have one last gander then head back to Soho. Madame Claudine's bound to have yer' pipe an' slippers ready.'

'I've gorra good tip for you'se two today. Vinny told me about it yesterday in graft. I'll slap a tenner each on now if yer' want.'

'Vinny might have the best tips on London shopping, but when it comes to the gee-gees he's nearly as bad as you! Nah, I'll keep me tenner, it's a tenner more for Big Time Charlie.'

Paddy agreed, before turning to me. 'How much you got in that account?'

'Mind yer' own business and start saving up soft shite!'

Leaving the café, we sauntered down the main shopping street trying our best to blend in with hordes of shoppers and foreign visitors. It wasn't hard merging with the Saturday throng, but it was instant recognition from locals the minute we opened gobs. I imagined what they'd think: *Three Scouse*

Scallywags in Windsor? They're obviously not History students?
Street conversation was kept bare minimum. Within shop
walls it was American, posh English, and anything but Scouse.
Yet to be engaged in small talk, breaking another rule, we
strolled past the window of the shop we'd just taken from as
another designer gaff lay a few doors down.

Without acknowledgement we entered. A gorilla with a
huge, walrus mustache greeted our entrance. He nodded, but
never spoke. It was Village People, Leatherman from the *YMCA*
song; six-foot six and an absolute eyeful. Dressed like a Kiwi
rugby player at an Airport terminal, he had black bell-bottomed
strides sailing above wedding cake heels, a black silk shirt open
to the tits with a silvery Epping Forest above its buttons, and a
head like a blown-up condom ready to burst. He stood out…a
bit! The chuckle-button baulked and twitched. Before clocking
him again I reeled myself in by swallowing hard.

Snaking between the watch springs of his chest lay a heavy
gold chain that looked like it had been tangled in his nettles for
twenty years. Silver wire jutted from his top lip or chest only,
while his head remained a shiny, 150 watt light bulb. The
beaming barnet, framed in black and floating in space, beamed
some more. This cat was either having his own seventies
revival here in the eighties, or he'd just kept on with the
seventies when everybody else had de-platform'ed and de-
flared. Paddy, biting hard on his top lip, eyed him, 'Uh Uh!
Watch out, it's that snooker player, Willie Thorne.'

Browsing the attire on offer, I stifled a laugh. I waited for
the Windsor disco king to speak…'Hiya fellers; can I help
either one of you find something today?'

The effeminate Julian Cleary voice was the pin to burst any
tense shoplifter's cheeks. Holding nothing back, we stood
there laughing…and laughing. Walrus Willie let out a long,
feminine sigh from what appeared to be clenched buck teeth.
You could tell he was goofy without looking as he almost
whistled. Politely guiding us to the door, he stood aside as we

chuckled ourselves out onto the pavement. Laughing loud, people stared. Willie popped his head around the door to see if we'd made tracks. We stared at his teeth, chest wire and wedding cake shoes, mesmerized once more; then burst into hysterics again!

Gathering composure, I nodded Boney out of the cafe as we headed back to the Station. Still tickled, we struggled to tell him what had gone on. Reaching the station, joke over, we knew we'd messed up. But, who cared? Windsor was dead; in other words: busy as towns go, but devoid of the decent clobber emporiums we wished for. The next train left in fifteen minutes. We had time to show Boney what tickled us. Taking him back to Willie Thorne's boutique, we told him to watch out for the silver-backed Gorilla hiding behind the coat rack. Outside, twiddling thumbs, with the swagbag on full view, we wondered what the curly-haired cowboy was upto. Toying with the idea of crossing the street to check proceedings, the door of Willie's boutique finally opened. With hardly a smirk, Boney approached. 'He wasn't that funny!'

'Why were you so long then?'

'Cos this softshite's done the damage; unlike two other softshite's you could care to mention! Right, let's do one!'

'What have yer' copped for Boney?' asked Paddy.

'Don't know? Err…eight or nine of them Dior shirts…I think?'

Entering the Station, we clocked the train about to shunt the buffers. Making our way to the platform a stern arm reached across my face. It belonged to the second hairy tash of the morning. A British Rail Gold hat barred my way. Gold hats, in charge of other Station Guards, took no excuses about dodgy tickets or non-payment. With not reaching the train yet, stopping us getting to the platform seemed somewhat premature?

'What's your problem mate? We're trying to make the train. It's leaving in a couple of minutes.'

'I know that sonny, you're too late. You should have boarded the train a few minutes ago. This train is ready to depart immediately.'

'But it's sitting there. Let us through will yer'?'

'Not on your life sonny! As I've already told you, it's too late. The train is about to leave on time.'

Hat to toe, I eyed him. He returned the compliment. He'd arrived at the concourse from planet Discipline, where a strict code of rules and regulations had to be observed at all times. The Sergeant Major of Windsor station, hairy top-lip an' all, stood true and strong. A scrubbed-red, brillo-pad-face beamed atop a brand new, immaculately presented British Rail uniform. This fella looked ready to invade Poland in defence of his station. I knew instantly he viewed us as bunkers and dawdlers, and that we'd stepped right to the heart of his battleground. Relaxing my stance, the demonstrative side of my nature checked, I eyed him once more. The three of us, hands on hips, stood bewildered, staring at the train idling on the platform. I took a breath. 'When's the next train then?'

'You should have read *the quite clearly signed* British Rail timetable further back Sonny-Jim.'

Patronizing prick, I'm thinking. Looking about in disbelief then staring hard at the train, we glanced at Gold Hat as he barred ours and a number of other people's paths to the platform. One lady, slight resemblance to Princess Anne, pushed to the front. 'What is your problem man? This young chap is perfectly correct in wanting to know why we can't get past you and your person to join the bloody train!'

Carrying a briefcase and wearing a waxed Barbour coat like Paddy's, though poles apart in accent, social class and their respective schemes in life, for a second they could have been sister and brother. For this one moment, never to be repeated, we were in the same boat, under the same banner, which read: *Get out the fucken' way jobsworth and let us join the train!*

Once I had the backing of ten or so, all trying to board, I went for it. Trying to move past the guard, he raised his arm. I ducked underneath. He dragged me back by the collar; stretching then ripping the stitching on my new Benetton crew neck jumper. The popping noise told me he'd torn off at least two buttons on the Lacoste polo shirt underneath. The popping buttons – red mist tablets – travelled from neck to brain, before detouring down sinews in my neck to clenched muscles in my arms. With human eruption orders gathering pace, the words simmered slowly, 'What the fffuck…are you…upto?'

Before he answered, I spelt it out. 'You…stupid…jobsworth…prick!'

Princess Anne butted in. 'You're a disgrace to the job man. I've seen you do this before; you silly, silly ignoramus!'

'Just doing my job M'aam; now step back if you would.'

'I'm going to report you to your supervisors. This is simply not on!'

As they went toe to toe, the train idled at the platform. Motioning towards it, I knew if things escalated Police intervention could mean big trouble for our little crew. First steps down the platform, collar straightened, I checked for damage, only to be severely yanked back again!

'I've told you once sonny-jim, or are you plain ignorant? Nobody is getting beyond this point and no more passengers will board that train! Is that clear enough for you?'

His cold nails digging into the skin of my neck were a yank too far. Get yer' stinking hand's off me nut job!'

He tried manhandling me yet again; I completely lost it. Hitting him with an over-the-shoulder right cross Lennox Lewis would have been proud of, I shuddered arm to toe. Legs turning to jelly, Jobsworth collapsed to the ground! Corporal punishment had been on the cards for him…now me! Another Kodak moment kicked-in. My memory had been jabbed with such ferocity that the moment became freeze-framed in time.

A small pool of blood formed the moment he hit the deck. It oozed from a gaping wound over his left eye, as small rivulets ran along the arch of his brow before dripping from the cliff of his face. I felt each minor explosion, as the droplets splashed onto the cold concrete floor. Gibbering and spluttering like a baby after feeding, people automatically backed-off. I looked toward my partners in crime. They seemed shell-shocked like the other commuters.

For the briefest, I entertained standing ground. Gold Hat had been way out of order...I had witnesses...Yeah, but I'd decked somebody in uniform. The witnesses had viewed my reaction to provocation before truly hearing my accent. They could be wavering, or at least questioning my reasons for being there? The swagbag Boney carried meant he'd surely fuck-up if asked questions by intervening Transport Plod – Time to skedaddle!

Princess Anne, recognizing my panicky demeanour, sweetly guided people aside like an Air Hostess clearing an aisle. Creating a human corridor of escape, I revved the engines. She turned to me. 'Good on you young man, I'd have done the same bloody thing myself if I had half the strength!'

Looking to the gathering, she pointed at me, 'This man was severely provoked. I for one bear witness he tried to board that train fairly!'

The gathering didn't look too convinced, instinctively turning toward the platform as the train left the station. And, thanks an'all that for your help ma'am but, mind made up, it was time for me to do likewise. Locking on Paddy and Boney, I made myself clear. 'If everything's sweet, see yer' at Claudine's in two hours!'

Grabbing the swagbag between Boney's feet, thinking: *if I'm going to flee, might as well take incriminating evidence with me,* I fled the station like Sebastian Coe viewing the finishing line. Zigzagging shopper's and tourist's full-tilt through the streets of Windsor, I rapidly put distance between the station and myself. Off in the distance, I slowed to walking pace, taking in means of transport available. Remembering we'd changed trains at Slough, a bus or Taxi back to Slough should get me a ride to London? It didn't seem a good idea; thinking Plod would've had a full description circulating the area in minutes?

Knowing the identification of Gold Hats attacker was all-important to any pursuer's, I entered Millets, an outdoor, camping shop, and lifted the shittiest, cheap cagoule on offer: the nylon, pea-green type that hill walkers wear to blend with the countryside? It was distinctly different from the grey Dunhill raincoat I now carried in a rolled-up bundle. After slotting the pea-green anorak, I followed it with a rainbow coloured, student scarf. Out of range of the outdoor stockists, I pulled the cagoule over my head and zipped it to the top. The rainbow scarf, worn university style, completed my *One Flew over the Cuckoo's Nest* out patient on his way back to the nuthouse appearance.

Asking an old lady where I could catch a bus to Slough, she pointed back in the direction of the station. That being a no-no, I stopped a Taxi and told the driver in a Farmer Giles accent to take me to Slough train station. In transit, I offered no reply to his polite conversational questions. He got the message loony-tunes, his silent passenger for the short journey, couldn't converse normally. Dropping loony-tunes outside the station, I paid him the exact fare with no tip on top. Being a true lunatic, I didn't understand tips.

Waiting for the London train at the platform, I carried on mirroring a poor lunatic on home leave. In trouble – act daft – stare at trains – speak in tongues – be innocent – be a total fool! This Hoisting game had me playing Andy McDaft so often I had the part to a tee. A guard, taking pity on me, came to the bench where I sat and told me the next train would be to London Paddington in ten minutes. Hoping the other two had jumped aboard I didn't hold much on that score. In their shoes, I'd have gotten well away from trains. They hadn't committed any offence inside the station, but if somebody pointed them out as the assailant's buddies? then mates, Officer Dibbles' questions would have no doubt begun in earnest. Anyway, reading graffiti inside Bizzie cells can be damn waste of a fine Saturday afternoon.

The London Train approached. Walking its full length, I checked the carriages. With no sign of either of them, I hoped they'd found alternative transport. Finding an almost empty train – strange for a Saturday afternoon – I realized none of the gathering around Sergeant Major Jobsworth had boarded? Minor detail games revved! The helpful guard, closing open doors departing passengers had lazily left ajar, reached where I stood. 'Make my job a lot easier if people had the courtesy to close doors behind them; you hopping aboard young man?'

'Yeah, err, yeah.'

Daydreaming like a half-decent dimwit, it looked like I'd ignored him. He gave a loud *tut!* Stepping up into the passageway, he slammed the door behind me. Pushing the window down, I shouted, 'Hey Mister, how long ago did the last train leave for London Paddington?'

'About twenty minutes ago young man. Things are running a little out of sync today, due to an earlier bit of bother on the line. Apparently somebody placed something on the track this morning. If you see a gang of railway workers about ten miles further on, they'll only be clearing the area of debris.'

'Ok. Mister; cheers for that.'

At least he hadn't used the 'point's failure' excuse. Thinking the others had caught a previous train, I took to watching the world go by in between the odd snooze. Arriving at Paddington, the boom of London life woke me; its cymbals hitting me square on. The place heaved. Weaving underground, I clocked the yellow Circle line to take me to Baker Street. Staring at the Underground track I watched mice scurrying between the rails: an underground world – underground! Not too dissimilar to the one above, where people scuttled out to get food before ducking back into their hidey-holes. At Baker Street I caught the Bakerloo line, before happily coming up for air at Piccadilly, where a short walk up Shaftsbury Avenue would bring me to Claudine's. Reaching the junction with Wardour Street, I had to turn left to find Berwick where the Fanny-Lenders den was situated. Peckish, I almost darted into Gerrard Street as a mixture of gorgeous aroma's wafted from Chinatown.

A glorious sun shone on a market in full-swing around Berwick Street. One king-size stall, selling every fruit known to man, dazzled the already carnival-like landscape, turning it into a jigsaw picture. Squinting to focus on the beautiful display drew me nearer the fantastic array of goods on offer, and, at the far corner of the stall stood Paddy and Boney, deep in conversation with Mr. Barrow boy himself. Waving their arms about in animated fashion, it felt great to see them. Moving through the crowd they couldn't see my approach. Up close, I let out a loud 'Boo!' Those in proximity jumped back, revealing the culprit, chastised and hugged in one motion.

'Alright Mickey' said Paddy, pleased to see me. 'Shit, yer' frightened the...how are yer' Mickey lad?'

'Alright Mickey, we back to graft then?' Boney flatly enquired.

Revealing our modes of transport for getting back to the City, Paddy surprised me saying Princess Anne had linked arms with them both, before leading them out of Windsor station to the front door of her house, half a mile away. Picking up the keys to her Mercedes, she drove them into London. Dropping them at Ealing Broadway Station, she told them about her frequent run-ins with the Gestapo like Station-master, saying the guy had upset people before with his lack of decent, common sense. The fact he'd been finally put on his arse came as no surprise to the Princess. When I'd fled, she said she could sense Paddy and Boney's anxiety, and knew they were associated with the guy who'd struck old Adolf – as she called him. Good deed for the day, she'd taken it upon herself to fetch the two of them to London.

Paddy, sex on the brain, told me that with the posh lady being so unnaturally nice to them, he'd misread the signals as a *come-on* towards himself. Thinking the lady might be requiring the services of the young Jimmy Dean, he tried chatting her up in the front seat. Strongly rebuking him, she told him not to push his luck. There you go, always a Princess in my book! He added the two of them had already left deposits at Madame Persia's sex-den, and they'd wait for me if required. Boney explained. 'I was getting a bit fed up with that Madame Claudine; she makes me hurry-up too much. It's deffo Madame Persia for me from now on!'

I asked him, 'Hey Bone, is it Madame, Miss, Miss or Madame, or what?'

'I'm not arsed either way; all I know is Miss Persia's the best shag!'

Saturday, being main earning day, I wanted to make the most. 'Listen, swagbag's only half-full, fancy a mosey on over to Knightsbridge? It's only a couple of stops to Harvey Nick's, Harrods and Beauchamp Place. Then there's Sloane Street up to Kings Road…all nearby?'

Getting approval, we headed back to Piccadilly to tube it to Knightsbridge. With my shifty outlook, I held the view we looked like three scallywags on a shoplifting expedition in the West-End – correctly so. But, unless you heard the accents, we could easily have passed for three friendly college graduates, chatting away, overcoat's over one arm, as we strolled up sunny Shaftsbury Avenue. Passing Hyde Park corner I mentioned *our* speech, and *its* speech-making history. Boney looked up from his newspaper. 'Never mind the way we talk, listen to this. It says here some woman called Madame Cynthia has been caught operating a Brass-gaff in Streatham, South London. It says the brothel was raided by Bizzies, and was full of weird whipping gear. What about us paying a visit to the gaff?'

Paddy laughed. 'Yer' getting a bit carried away with the sex thing aren't yer' Boney mate. Those places are for pervy men in pinstriped suits.'

'I'm only thinking about a better bunk-up.'

Snatching the newspaper, I sussed his deadpan expression then the headline. 'Boney, shut the fuck up! And Paddy, stop confusing the poor lad.'

Pulling into Knightsbridge, I read about notorious brothel keeper, Cynthia Payne. 'Boney…think it's time you gorra proper bird; yer' Brass-mad. Yer' gonna catch a dose, or end up one of them fella's who begs a Prozzie to marry him.'

'About time yer' gorra proper bird yerself mate!' He replied.

'Ha! Listen to the twenty-three year old virgin, just broke his duck in Soho! Come on, Harrods is around the corner. Be careful mind; it's rammed with Floorwalkers this toffee-nosed gaff! As we're here, it's worth a-once-over; nothing ventured, nothing gained an'all that.'

Paddy nodded. 'Harrods it is old bean. Listen, go in separate, we'll meet in the men's department, Ok.'

Visiting the famous department store weekly, we noted Floorwalkers and security all over the show; but if you knew the right angles you could avoid getting an inside tail or an outside knock-back from the green uniformed, La-di-da men. Getting turned away the week before, two jolly green giants had overheard our Liverpool accents. Giving us the SS eyeball, they head-stamped us as undesirables. We referred to them as La-di-da doormen because posh accents with a hoity-toity facade, you were a citizen; loud, coarse accents, with a rapscallion demeanour, and it was *use the revolving door please gents!*

It didn't take long to realize American accents opened London doors. Well…the ones normally rammed straight in your gob. If they wanted John Wayne as Rooster Cobourg, then it was JR from Dallas they were going to get. Dallas, a popular Ameri-soap, based on a family of oil tycoons, was loved by millions of viewers. Those telly-mad millions, meant time for me to pump my crude impersonation at the jolly green giant on door patrol.

'Howdy pardner.'

I nearly laughed as La-di-da dutifully held the door open; my American Express, expression, accepted. The weekly soap drama was Top of the Pops; so, being a man of popular culture with a raging lifting habit, I studied JR Ewing the megalo-maniac, main protagonist, whenever he appeared on TV. His southern drawl didn't marry too well to the chuckle button, but a man's gorra do what a man's gorra do. Each day JR's accent became part of my admission speech repertoire. Any jurisdiction over laughter control could easily be lost in the shop doorway, especially if the other two came too close. If Boney tried, we'd be creased first sentence; and that first sentence would be put into a recognition box and sent packing. Being useless at mimicry, we'd waste an age rolling about as the would-be actor tried to act.

Separating, I made my way to the lift. The attendant opened and closed the sliding door. I gave him a curt 'Thaaank you sur,' but, unbeknown to me, Paddy and Boney had been up and down twice and, hearing my Dallas accent as I entered, Paddy laughed out loud. *Well,* I'm thinking, *end of story;* till he pretended he had a private joke with Boney. Reaching menswear, a quick scan revealed no tail, but smudges (ceiling cameras) hovered like dark spaceships above.

Lifting ledger: One place you never ignore the cameras prying eye is a department store. Super-duper, poseur-friendly emporiums like Harrods employed security to sit and monitor the building and its floor space: a sort of robber's reality TV. You'd basically ignore smaller shops cameras: installed for proof in court, staff theft, or for salespeople to check somebody acting suspiciously. For scanning purposes we found a cosy speck at the back of the shop – as a lifter often does.

Bringing the right garments to the trenches (the back wall) they got slotted smoothly into the inside coat lining. With the rest of the shop floor in sight, Boney, holding up a sweater, covering our action, meant we slotted on cue. An expansive floor space could mean *hopefully* rather than *definitely* regarding camera's eye. Harder to scan and more difficult to detect anything untoward, Hoisting game odds shorten drastically inside department store jungles.

Having a final gander round one of the priciest gaffs on earth told me the moment of skedaddle had a flashing green light. Likewise signals got banded between the three of us. Once all signals came back affirmative, it was fresh-air time. Leaving separately, in case one of us had been sussed, left two to walk away, able to mount a challenge to a would-be-captor by creating a diversion. Lifting ledger: We'd promised to not get physical with Floorwalkers, Bizzies or shop-staff, a different ball game, with stiffer sentences for stiffer fists. At the Chicken Coops one night, we concluded violence towards ordinary shop staff was a complete no-no. Paddy and me, clear about having no problem jumping on a Floorwalker, agreed we'd never let it reach that point. Windsor's Mr. Gold Hat had reached my point, I suppose. But street or shop wrestling, or anything physical, we outlawed, and rightly so.

I'd binned five pair of formal pants, and never heard of the Italian designer on the label. A price tag of eighty pounds each taught me all I needed to know. Vinny placed expensive formal wear at the top of the shopping hitlist. It felt strange taking the lift to ground floor with five pair of pants stuffed aboard, but any private thoughts on the matter got interrupted by three stocky Australians, whom I'd sussed trying to dip the purse from some rich old biddy's bag. Looking like middleweight boxers, they gave me the once over. As things unfurled, they threw me a further look that said, *mind your business, or you could be in for a dig once the ding-dong sounds at ground floor.* Not easily intimidated, I carried on ear-wigging their accents and blimping their sly technique.

Suited and booted, the three of them – dipping game apart – could've passed for a posse of tough looking, Antipodean gold mine owners out visiting Harrods while in London on business. The angriest looking stuck his neck out, giving me pumping veins and his best hard-case glare. He turned deeper red when I smiled straight back into his train-tracked face. No Aussie sun could get rid of those blade-inflicted mars bars (scars). They knew I wasn't security, but they knew I had them sussed and, how unmoved I was by their gangsters-down-under glares.

Feeling the dull weight of the swag I carried, I looked back at them. *Australian pickpockets working the lifts in Harrods;* it was a new one on me. I presumed some Fagin-type urchin firm from Canning Town would've had this little enterprise boxed-off long ago. I'd also presumed any outsiders looking to earn on mainline Cockney turf, like this Aussie team, would be swiftly warned-off, cut, or pavement splattered. London's streets widened my eyelids daily.

Reaching ground floor, ready to scarper, the Aussies stepped back into the lift. Like a dickhead I followed suit. Don't ask why, I just did. The old lady, minus her purse, innocently sloped off at ground level. Three other people entered. No sooner the doors closed than the hard-case glares began again. Seriously intrigued by the three snarling Aussie's, the lift bounced and I got jolted to reality and the stupidity of being nosey. Time to change lifts next stop. Coming to a halt, I waited impatiently for the doors to open but, before I got the chance to step out, the angriest with the Frankenstein scars motioned. 'G'day squire, you gotta problem?'

The doors opened slowly. About to be Wallabee'd in the lift, I answered and escaped sharpish. 'It wasn't you

Aborigines I was clocking it was the wallet you dropped on the floor.'

Bowing shoe-ward they scanned the empty lift. Doors closing, I shouted inside, 'One-nil to England, you fucken' Aussie knobheads!' as the doors slammed shut.

Childish – maybe – but it allowed me the luxury of a dignified exit, while rattling the snarler's cages; something those well-mannered English bowlers might want to take on board. Leaving the building, I waltzed past the La-di-da men to greet a dazzling sun. Sweat dripping from my brow, I scanned surroundings for the other two. Straight ahead, they sat atop a steel mesh fence separating cars from pedestrians on Brompton Road. Noting a meeting direction when splitting into Harrods was a must; the snooty joint had a stack of exits. Drawing close, Paddy looked uneasy, 'Mickey, you on top or what? Three suits on the way up; seem to be bang on your tail?'

Turning, I viewed the three Aussie's marching and gesturing in an angry manner. Brompton Road's battle of the Ashes looked set to go off. I explained, 'Don't worry, they're not security. It's a team of Australian Dippers I've just had a bit of a run-in with, that's all. Don't get off just yet. Let's see what they want.'

Fast approaching, confrontation looked imminent. Paddy and Boney jumped from the fence. But, the three pickpockets surprisingly walked straight past. Looking back towards Harrods I noticed security men accompanied by La-di-da's leaving the store in pursuit of the Australians. 'Hmm...time to make ourselves scarce. Don't do any leggers, just walk. I'm sure they're tailing the angry mob. Come on, this way.'

Walking past Brompton Place, I signalled a turn into Brompton Gardens. 'Yeah, down here. This is the one.'

Glancing back, we could see security crossing Brompton Road and leaping the mesh fence that took you away from Brompton Gardens. Paddy, relieved he didn't have to run, blew air. 'Yeah, it's alright.'

Checking back again, the three Aussies sprinted into the distance, jackets flapping in the breeze as the Harrods Plod Squad played catch-up. Boney squinted intently, 'Shall I go back in for a fill? I haven't binned anything yet.'

'Might be right you know, security being busy.' added Paddy.

'Nah, come on, leave that for now. You know…never return to the scene an'all that. Beauchamp Place is up here; it's crawling with boss designer shops anyway.'

On our way we bumped into Cecil Gee, the men's designer chain store. Noticing Cecil's had alarm barriers inside the door we walked to an entry further on to stash the swagbag. We wanted three people inside and didn't need the bag bringing extra attention. Some places we didn't care, but Cecil's, A1 formal threads, meant we did. Boney entered first. Thirty seconds later, we did likewise.

With security tagging not so prevalent Hoisting gangs were less clued up on how to remove tags from clothing; so, we started a simple ruse you could hit a shop for on just one occasion. Firstly: when the chance arose, tags or no tags, two of you would load-up with anything on offer. Secondly: The third person in your firm, knowing you were loaded and ready to go, would draw the attention of a shop assistant to convince her/him of his interest in purchasing an expensive item of clothing; say…a £300 suede jacket, and he would like to try it on for size. Wearing the item, assuring the assistant he wanted to make the purchase, he'd start walking about the store, checking the feel and suitability of the coat. Thirdly: Questioning the dimness or brightness of shop lighting, before the assistant could stop him, he'd step outside the door in search of natural daylight. With exit alarm boxes instantly activated, as an un-tagged garment left the premises, shop-staff, alerted by the door alarm, normally came running. Fourthly: Meanwhile, as the system had already been set-off, his two accomplices, loaded and waiting, could walk out above suspicion. Only worth the risk for expensive or hard to get items, Cecil Gee's was worth it.

Innocent shoppers leaving with a newly purchased item have often jumped with fright when a door alarm has gone off, due to forgetful staff not de-tagging the garment. Or, not so innocently, someone like us has purposely dropped a security tag in the bag, triggering the alarm, so as to assist a lifters exit with a decent fill on board. You could always play 'drop-tag' if you were Hoisting alone. I did it on Oxford Street to an old biddy and got the big guilt trip when she was escorted back into the store to be searched and questioned.

With Boney Yankee-blagging the Cecil Gee guy how he loved the fit and feel of the coat, in his own patter, Paddy and I battled to suppress laughter. Remaining out of earshot to not hear conversation, you'd still catch a snippet to jab at the chuckle button. Setting Cecil's door bleepers off, Boney was no innocent shopper. No sooner he stepped outside with the serving Lionel Blair in tow, than Paddy and I waltzed onto the pavement; the door alarm acting as starting gun to exit. The all-dancing, Lionel, only concerned with Boney stepping back into the store, also waltzed, trying to usher him back inside. He needed to de-activate the alarm system and inform other staff why the bleepers had sounded in the first place.

Boney, a natural for acting the dope, was in no hurry to hear Lionel's pleas about re-entering Cecil Gee's, giving us more time to escape. Crossing the main Brompton Road we waited for him to reappear. A minute later his curly bonce hit daylight. The familiar whistle sounded. With Boney's sight and attention, the whistle was a must. His vision, ignorance to Floorwalker and camera detail, and overall doziness made him obvious Bagman. But, tagged shops remained an exception. Up close, he asked, 'Everything sweet?'

'Yeah, sweet as.'

'Did you'ze get anything half-decent?'

'Two suede jackets, two hundred nicker apiece; lovely coats. Vinnie'll like these alright.' Paddy quipped.

'What did yer' tell Lionel Blair about the coat Bone? You learned anything this week?' I asked.

'I told him I was gonna change some Dollars at the Bureau De Change, like yer' said, and that I'd be back in ten minutes. Anyway, what d'yer' mean by learning?

'Don't be so paranoid Boney lad! Listen, these jackets should get us at least seventies. Few more bits, then switch-off time. Saturday night, Illford Palais, here we come!'

Switch-off had me thinking about my Big Time Charlie account and a night out with wedge in pocket. Eager to breathe easy, I kept my eyes peeled on Cecil's door to be sure there was no tail…Sweet! Walking to Beauchamp Place, a small poseur's street with an assortment of designer shops, a couple more earners showed face. Finished with Beauchamp, ready to trek east to McRents, we turned into Pont Street and the busier main road of Sloane. Dunhill's emporium, a short walk away and a place we'd frequented, got me dib-dabbling with the idea of heading straight in. When in doubt, head on out!

With so many rip-off designer shops based along the so-called glamorous stretches of West London, it was tempting to keep pushing your luck. Marching about the London streets meant parchment, with a Saturday drink never far from thought. Caught between two tube stations, we pondered whether to go back to Knightsbridge, or carry on up Sloane Street to Sloan Square. A string-vested, old tramp, spread-eagled on the grass in a small park at Cadogan Place, shouted over in a broad Irish accent, 'Can one of you young feller's spare a bit of change ferra' bevvy please?'

Seamus McNesbitt, fifteen years prior to Rab C, unwittingly made our minds up. Admiring his honesty in not giving the usual beggars hard-luck story, we laughed at his temerity. Gathering the sought after nicker-for-the-liquor, he gave many a 'thank-you young Scouse' proclamations, and followed them with a thousand blessings in poetic Irish blarney. My expensive Dunhill coat, not having that brand new sheen, and the Jocks owning a wardrobe full, had me offering it to Seamus. Though way too small to stretch around his poisoned belly, he snaffled it like it was the Golden Fleece.

Turning towards Knightsbridge, Paddy's worn out tube map told us we could catch the Piccadilly line to Holborn, then change for the Central line to Bethnal Green. We'd organised to meet Vinny in a local boozer, to drop anything lifted that day. The ordinary down to earth people of Bethnal Green suited us to a tee. Though we were flush, we were never going to be flash!

I'd learned early in Liverpool that you could find a host of Bogus Bums hogging the phoney limelight inside glitter ball discotheques like the Hippodromes of this world; along with the rest of the divvy, big-city, bright light's brigade. West End... no sirree, deffo not for me: big trucks, spending big bucks, acting like daft fucks! I'd never been attracted to that kind of dance. It was like me ol' fella used to say: 'Big Time Charlie's – usually heading for Big Time comedowns!' Speaking to him on the phone about London life, I hoped he hadn't included my flush new Bank account in that statement.

KEEP TALKING

Saturday night I was set to meet a bezzy mate of Paddy's new flame. He'd said she was a looker. 'Wish I'd have copped-off with the other one, she's miles better looking. Gorra lovely pair of melons as well. Might be a bit loopy, but who cares if she's not the full-shilling if she's dangerous on the nest?'

It was time I stopped copping for clobber and started copping-off otherwise I'd be pitching in for a Soho season ticket with Boney! Paddy hadn't had to sell me the idea. Entering Illford Palais, Boney was at the bar with Terry and a kid called Danny Felman, but I was a man on a mission. With Terry's girl studying up in Oxford he'd asked to tag along. He was always welcome. After a few pints with Vinny in Bethnal Green we'd shot back to McRents to get changed and pick up the Spanner.

Boney and Terry talked endlessly about music and got along well. I'd also introduced Boney to a lad called Danny Felman, who'd told me one night inside the Palais that he was an ex-gambling addict. Thinking he'd set Boney on a different course to a racing course, I helped get them pally. Now they were a drinking threesome. Boney sorted, I hoped the two girls wouldn't arrive till late. Being honest, I was getting desperate for a bunk-up, not a female drinking partner for the night.

Knowing a lot of Palais regulars, being regulars ourselves, if I'd been alone it would have been easy to find company. Soon as Paddy notified me the ladies had walked in I found I'd been jumping the gun assuming we'd be stuck with them for the night. Noticing Michelle, my lady in waiting, she walked straight over. First impressions: a young Leslie Ash in cult Mod-film, Quadrophenia, before she turned her lips into mudguards. In an Essex, Mockney accent, Michelle piped up. 'Suppose your Mickey sweetheart! Yeah, my mate said you were decent looking. Now, don't let that go t'yer' head and I'll see you in a few hours; bit a gossip to catch up on, see. Catch yer' later darling! Oh, by the way, if you're carrying a nice bag of Charlie, don't forget to bring me my share; ta ta for now!'

No sign of shyness there then. And off she toddled in her white stilettos, knockers under her chin and a bum like two junior school volleyballs wrapped in a tea towel. She was dolly material alright. Seemed Paddy had marked her card with the loopy description though. Judging by the front she had (not her bosom), which I wasn't used to, her asking straight-up if I had any clam chowder got me thinking this wasn't your average Vera. Not being a snorter, a sniffer or a swallower, and still drug naïve about Cocaine Cuties like Michelle, I'm thinking, *go with the flow*.

'Where are these birds from Paddy?'

'Told yer' she was lovely, didn't I?'

'Yeah, she sure is, but where are they from?'

'Romford, it's in Essex, why?'

'I've heard all about these Essex birds. I'm wondering why she's not with a fella, cos she's definitely a beauty alright?'

'She packed him in the other week. Why? Getting cold feet? Swap if yer' want?'

'Her ex-fella probably didn't have a big enough bag of Charlie!'

'Is that what she asked yer' for? Weirdo! Lovely looking

bird riddling herself with that shite! Anyway, I mean it; I'll swap if yer' want?'

Checking Michelle throughout the night she'd be surrounded by an audience with *her* lips the only ones blabbing. Few slow songs at the end – Patti Labelle singing *on my own* – and I winked at Boney and made a move. Patti finished, smooching over, we parted with a peck on the lips. Michelle wanted to find Debbie, so I made my way back to the bar to finish my drink. With doormen calling time, I wandered to the exits.

Spotting Paddy, standing with the ladies, they waved me over and we left as a foursome. Though we'd left the Club her electric lips still jigged to the music. Talking non-stop about clothes, she'd suddenly break midstream to talk about starving children in India. Next minute: state of the England football team and, getting to the centre forward, she'd switch channels and start on about some TV documentary on Scott of the Antarctic. Putting it down to too much talc up the nose, we carried on walking back to McRents. Suddenly the conversation joined the Twilight Zone. Telling me about her Clampitt family and her four cranky brothers I'm not getting a word in edgeways and, as there's only so much shite you can listen to for the sake of a bunk-up, I joked, 'Listen Michelle, any chance of getting a word in?'

She stopped for the briefest, 'Go on don't let me stop ya!'

'These four brothers yer' on about, do they look after yer' and so-forth? I mean, yer' know the way brothers are supp…' and she butts-in, 'Nah, don't need no looking after me. Ask anyone, I can look after meself, no danger. With those four on me case since I was…' Reaching into her blue suede shoulder bag, still speaking, she pulls out this Crocodile Dundee dagger, the fish-skinning ones with a serrated blade. Leslie Ash and her Lecky lip's had just turned into the witch from the Wizard of Oz. *Bunk up or no bunk up*, I'm thinking, *it's not worth the hassle mate. Get out of this one…?*

Meantime, we're getting further and further away from Paddy and Debbie, and closer and closer to McRents. Walking slower up Cranbrook Road she sensed my change of pace and stopped mid-story. 'Why we walking so slowly? Not scared of losing yer' mate are ya?'

'Nah, the weather's lovely; enjoying the fresh air.'

Inside I'm going: *once she sees the walk-in wardrobe I live in, after Paddy giving it the big one I'm a top earner with prospects an' all that, she'll shiv me!*

Walking behind garden bushes to relieve myself gave me respite. I'm thinking again: *Could piss off through the backs of these houses? But Paddy and Debbie are right behind. They're bound to meet Looney Tunes and bring her back to McRents.*

'Mickey, come on love, I'm starting to feel the cold. It makes me think of all those starving kids in Calcutta; and these pants cost forty quid, would yer' believe it? My Dads been to Calcutta yer' know; he should've fackin' stayed there! Did you see that telly programme about an earthquake in Califor…'

Blah, blah, bleeding blah, she's off again. I couldn't even give it a shake in peace. 'Come on Michelle, not far now.'

'Mickey, do you know where my mate Debbie is? Oh there she is…it's all right. Do you go to the Palais a lot then?'

'The odd Sa…'

'Cos I think I've seen you there before. Whereabouts do you work then?'

'The two of us work on a buil…'

'My job does my bleeding head in! Does Paddy work with you then?'

'Yeah! We've both been wor…'

'Cos my mate Debbie, she's sort of boss hairstylist, so I can get time off and stuff no problem. What sort of music do you like?'

'I like Pink Floy…'

'Cos I like that guy from Wham, the one who puts the

shuttlecock down his shorts, and that Scottish group, Big Country, yer' know, the ones that make the guitars sound like bagpipes. My dad's Scottish. Dianna Ross she's the boss, ha ha ha. And what about *Shout, shout, let it all out, these are the things you can do without, a come on' I'm talking to you, so come...'*

She's pointing at me singing this Tears for Fears song full-pelt, and I'm thinking, *Weirdo, Weirdo, Weirdo*...funny, but not funny though!

'*I'm talking to you, so come on*. Join in, or don't yer' know the words? And erm, erm, I like that sexy feller from The Style Council. What's his name?'

'Paul Weller?'

'Not him, the other guy in the blazer with the curly blonde hair. What kind of clothes do you like? Cos I like...'

Giving up completely, she blabbed me to the front door. Unable to get a word in, I opened the door and pointed upstairs. She continued talking her way into my Chicken Coop. She stopped momentarily for breath when I put a firm finger to her lips. She might wake Clifford, who was Ok, or the Denim Dyke who was not Ok! Her miserable, whinging gob was bound to make anyone angry, and with Michelle carrying the Essex Excalibur in her handbag of many colours...

Opening the door to my walk in wardrobe, I grabbed Michelle. Trying to shut her up, I darted my tongue into her mouth. It worked...for twenty seconds; then I kissed the only girl who ever managed to gab with a tongue wrapped around her own. Tongue-tangled, like she was teaching me how to move my tongue to talk, she muttered something about a tapping noise at the window. Pushing the flimsy curtain aside, I viewed Boney, Terry, Paddy and Debbie all looking for ammo to throw up at the glass. Boney couldn't remember where he'd left his keys. Paddy, still two'd-up with Boney, hadn't bothered to have a set made. Throwing mine down, I clocked the time. Sunday was a Hoisting no-no – to do with the Sabbath, and three catholic boys who still had a guilty conscience and the last remnants of some morality.

Putting an old Marvin Gaye cassette into the player got both of us in the mood. As Marvin sang *'Let's get it on'* Michelle's gorgeous white chocolate Easter eggs were deftly lifted from their packaging. Her finally making the right noises got me realizing my day job had taught me the right way to open wrapped goods. Caressed by Marvin's voice we became more intimate and loving. Though Michelle at one stage had turned into a witch, she now reverted back to the first impression she made on me: an absolute beauty! Once she stopped gabbing my brain clicked into fantasy mode, as I kissed and caressed what amounted on the surface to a dream girl...

But, like every dream or fantasy, someone or something has to ring the reality bell and supply a swift kick to the balls to land you firmly back on planet Witch! No matter the mood, or time, Michelle could not stop those electric lips from spoiling the moment. An hour or two of playing warming, hoochie coochie, interspersed with a hundred moment-zapping, cold Jackanory stories and I was again looking for a way out. To her amusement, when canoodling, I started calling her Lecky Lips, and, when she stopped me with an abrupt 'No!' after the third time I tried to open the zip on her pants, box-room reality and the thoughts of the dagger in the bag hit home.

Paddy eventually knocked around five in the morning, saying Boney was knackered, stoned and aching for kip. Him and Terry, while listening to some new albums in Terry's bedsit, had smoked their way through a baseball bat sized joint. Paddy, meanwhile, had been having his own private wrestling match in Boney's bedsit, where his new flame, according to Paddy, bounced him all over the ring. When Paddy told me about Boney being stoned on a spliff supplied by Clifford, in payment for some lifted, obscure reggae albums, I said, 'Boney, stoned! What's all that about? He's been stoned since the day he left his Ma's belly!'

185

Before she left, Michelle commented on the amount of labelled clothing hanging around the walls, and the fact things like cassette players, clocks and other gadgets seemed shiny and new. She added I'd have to get myself a new flat with more space before she returned. Returned! Who was she kidding? True, she had a scorching tongue, but it was burning into my brain around the lughole department, not at the back of my tonsils where it should have been. I got thinking: *upset no one, you know what they say about a woman scorned – especially the blade carrying variety!* Shame, she was a stunning lady to look at, but, I mean, you couldn't ask for a return visit on the proviso she let me apply three rolls of masking tape around her gob!

One thing I'd picked up from Michelle's incessant blabbering was most towns in Essex, according to her, were one-horse, no class shitholes! I'd tried quizzing her about Basildon, Romford, Chelmsford and some other towns east, but she'd given me the same answer each time – shitholes! From the dimmest bulb in the DIY store to the brightest star in heaven, I was constantly looking for info from Southerners I met on my travels. One of Vinny's crew usually knew, but it never stopped me doubling up.

At five o'clock in the morning I sought the communal pay phone near the kitchen. The local cab firm gave me a pick-up time of fifteen minutes. Having a final tongue wrestle of the night, I noticed a rusting, old staple-gun lying on the entrance window sill, along with some discarded stationery belonging to our Scottish gangster landlord. I grasped I should've picked up the staple-gun on the way in and stapled Michelle's tongue to her bottom lip. Too late now, she was plugged in again.

Standing in the doorway, front door open, everyone pretended to listen to Michelle's gibberish. When the cabbie arrived I noticed her gabbing her way in, getting herself comfy before starting a fresh assault on his virgin lug holes. My brain and ears were gagging for the beautifully laid-back *Pillow of*

Winds song, my very own go to sleep ballad, but hearing sensors were so numb that Roger Waters and David Gilmour didn't have to bother flexing tonsils to send me to dreamland.

Sunday came, Sunday went, another weekend of earning and learning gone by. Though Boney and I called Sunday *the Lord's Day*, in reality, it became switch-off day. Too drunk to mooch or too Catholic to Hoist, who knows? 'Got nothing to do with god', Paddy reckoned.

Getting into work Monday, the worst day for most, changed in our circumstances as Vinny presented us with the cash from whatever he'd turned over that weekend. Referring to it as The Monday Bung, if I'd had my way, it would've been a Monday only payday, but Paddy and Boney were constantly on the lookout for a midweek sub. In a city full of sharks, I trusted Vinny implicitly with the cash. In Cockney patter, he was a diamond geezer! Though I'd suffered with burnt fingers before, I had no problems banking Hoisting money with him. Learning to read between the lines and getting the right vibes about someone, due mainly to shoplifting, I'd become a people watcher. Anyway, he was doing us a favour getting rid of the swag so quickly. Any extra bunce he made on the side was his business because, come Monday, the Bung was slapped on the table!

Dressing formally for Hoisting duty, the site hut held three smart suits at the ready. The City of London, swamped with double-breasted, office-bods at lunchtime, meant we blended immaculately, till lips shifted. The Monday after getting my ears savaged by Michelle, we knocked at the door of what we called Alf Ramsey's dugout. Entering, Vinny sat expectantly with three cups of tea. The Monday Bung got pushed across the shabby, tea-stained table, thus bringing a little colour and brightness to the dullest part of the forty-hour working week.

Monday morning's sit-down felt like a motivational, start-of-the-week, team-talk. If we weren't coming up with a new earning scheme, or scam, Vinny would be putting his out-of-town ideas across. Knowing our intent about earning extra dough, he told us about other shopping areas in and around London that were not so obvious or well trodden as Kings Road or Oxford Circus. Regaling us with tales of Hoisting gangs he knew, and their favourite Home County hot spots around the city's perimeter, we referred to them as M25 towns. Not having constant wheels, it depended on whether the southern rail network could take you there; but reliable drivers were soon put in place in our quest for earners.

Monday Bung pocketed, we settled to a hot cuppa. Asking what type of weekend we'd had, and having briefed him about Saturday's escapades, Vinny talked about a fella paying a visit that afternoon who might put us onto a good earner. Surprising us with news he came from our neck of the woods, Boney asked, 'Yer' mean he's from Illford then Vinn?'

'Soft ollies, he's from Liverpool!'

That afternoon, back at the dug-out, we giggled when Vinny said Left Foot Lenny was on his way. However, when Left Foot barged through the door without formal introduction to swiftly park his arse opposite the three of us on the bench, nobody smirked. I'd imagined his left foot mangled or overgrown. It looked normal. He caught me glancing under the table before introducing himself as Lenny Edwards. Explaining the moniker, he said a wag down the pub who had heard all about Lenny's shoe robbing capers had given him it. If we listened up, we might be interested in what he had to say. It was good to hear him speak in a Liverpool accent – always a welcome sound to hear a native of your own city once you've strayed from home turf.

Lenny told us he had been abroad with his London born wife and kids on numerous occasions, and while driving through Northern Europe on sightseeing trips he'd noticed most shoe shops left the right shoe out on display. In England, it was always the left shop owners put out for customers to view or try for size. He added he'd been going abroad on weekend Hoisting trips with the *sole* intention of gathering as many left footed shoes and trainers as possible. Lenny would drive a hired van to the port of Folkestone or Dover, catching the car ferry to Oostende, Calais or first departing boat cross channel. Setting out Friday or Saturday morning, he'd return home two days later with a van full of left foot trainers, dress shoes, sandals or boots; anything except cheap Scooby Doo's (shoes) or slippers. Hoisting from only the most expensive, fashionable men's and ladies retail displays, of which there were thousands around Northern Europe, he'd named it his Foot Round.

God knows what the ripped-off footwear retailers of Belgium, Holland, France and West Germany managed to do with their outstanding stocks of right-peg only footwear? Maybe they employed pushy American salesman to sell them to Vietnam vet amputees...or something? I know: minor details? According to Lenny, a lot of the same brands and shops traded in the UK, meaning: most right foot items were easy to find in the city centre High Streets of Great Blighty. Sticking to pricey, expensive brands, like your Bally and Russell Bromley meant bigger profits.

Lenny reckoned his little enterprise might be about to come 'on top', as his frequent shoe-trips-abroad were getting noticed by the Her Majesty's Customs Officer's at the southern ports of England. He'd been pulled over the odd time when arriving back in the UK, driving off the boat at Dover. One officer noted the many weekend visits cross-channel he was making. Getting paranoid about the excuse he'd given for his left-foot-load – something about samples for his sisters shoe shop – he thought the van and his blag might be thoroughly turned over next time. He said it was time for new faces to carry the left-foot flag, implementing different cross-channel routes so the lone shoe enterprise could carry on unhindered.

I instantly had visions of a Customs Officer sitting around during tea-break, saying to his bosses: *'Hey Guvnor, we've had notification the Left foot mob have boarded the Calais boat arriving in a couple of hours. We'll give them a tug to see if we can find any Weed heels or maybe a few Cocaine brogues in the samples. You could get a fair amount of Charlie in a leather boot Guvnor.* I told Vinny and Lenny we'd think about it over the coming week and let them know soon as poss.

While the bosh over the head brigade would see this as too much like hard work, I always enjoyed a bit of ingenuity being a part of one's earners. Bosh over the head, or hurting people directly, or indirectly through drugs, savings scams etc, was all brain-fade crime to me, with the certain penalty of instant karma. Non-violence and no direct suffering to individuals was logged as do-able – a potential earner. The old shop excuse about pushing-up prices due to Hoisting was a load of old-bollocks! Those retail warriors with material dreams would put prices up come-what-may!

Family and upbringing had always taught me that institutions, big businesses and boardrooms were riddled with about as much corruption as you could imagine. Left Foot Lenny went on to own a string of shoe shops in his own right, err…left, and it's easy to work out how he stocked his first premises. But, Hoisting or no Hoisting, he'd be looking for maximum, rip-off profit once he joined the so-called honest world. Give me an honest thief to a lying businessman… anyday.

Later that day, digging footings where a large perimeter wall was to be built, I told the lads what I thought about Lenny's shoe graft. 'Not that good is it? I mean, we already earn decent dough at the weekend. And, I don't fancy getting a tug of the customs fellers. Once those bastards are on yer' case… what d'yer' think Paddy?'

'Nah, Fuck that! I haven't even got a passport. I sold it to some Pakistani fella for two hundred nicker on the way home from Germany last year.'

'Ha, yer' kidding aren't yer? How'd that come about?'

'Remember that building work I got in Cologne? Well, it only lasted four weeks. When we came home via Dover, one of the lads with us said he was selling his Pazzy in a shop outside Victoria Station. I sold mine in the same take-away for two hundred quid. A lot of fellers returning from graft did the same.'

'You'll regret that yer' know.'

'Why's that?'

'Well…what if we took off to Holland for some shoe graft? That's you out of the equation.'

'I'm not even arsed. If I wanna go abroad, I'll get me own false Pazzy.'

'Ha ha, yeah, Ok Paddy; sell yer' own passport t'go and buy a false one. That makes sense. What about you Bone? You be Ok?'

'I think it'd be alright if we got them Cuban heels Brumble wears and filled the heel with Charlie. And then…'

'Hang on a sec.' I interrupted, 'I'm only asking if you've got a Pazzy or not soft-shite! I'm not asking if yer' wanna be the next Tony Montana!'

'Err, nah! I've got no passport either.'

'Ok. End of that one, simple really! Listen, if we get the footing's dug I'll ask Vinny about an early dart around four'ish to go shopping.'

Normal Labourers usually tidied up at the end of the day, but with Clerk of Works holding vested interest in his Labourers outside activities, where early darts were proving mutually beneficial, this site ran differently. Knocking at the door of the dugout, Vinnie asked if I fancied a brew.

'Yeah…kill for one. Listen Vinn, footing's are dug, and I think most trades are packing away. We Ok for an early dart? Few shops to visit an'all that. Otherwise they'll be closed around half-five.'

'You boys wanna slow down. Anyway, the football's on when yer' get home.'

'We're never in a rush to get back to that place Vinny.'

'No problem Mickey. All the deliveries are in and seeing as its miserable bleeding Monday make yourselves scarce after a cuppa.'

I'd forgotten to deposit the Monday bung at Barclays. It could wait till tomorrow. Calling Paddy and Boney over, the evening routine of cleaning up before slipping into sharp togs began. Paddy, supping tea and changing, asked, 'That new Next shop, down the road, it's fully open now. Shall we take a gander?'

'Yeah, why not; come on Boney lad, you'll have it dark the rate your going.'

Walking off site, a couple of Brickies new to the job had noticed our departure. 'Alright for some, never heard of labourer's leaving early; you got something going with the boss then?'

'Don't be fucken' nosey, and get on with yer' work!' Boney countered.

Paddy looked shocked. 'This London life is definitely bringing you out of yer' shell Boney boy!'

'Trade or no trade, they've only been on the job ten minutes and their asking questions; pair of dickheads!'

As the Next store drew close, giving a quick finger to the lips, I pointed to a place on the pavement where Boney could keep a bleary eye on things. 'Try not to look suspicious ay Boney.'

Entering, I whispered to Paddy, 'Yankee Doodle' letting him know we were American again. London staff, used to serving rich Yanks, meant any mishap with voice interpretation would probably go unnoticed by servers already smelling American Express. Shop-staff approached: guy, thirty-ish, bit like Woody Allen; glasses, thin, bit nerdy if you know what I mean. 'Afternoon gents; if you need any assistance, I'm Andy, just give me a sign.'

'Hi man! Think we're okay for now; just looking for

something comfortable for a long flight home. I'll let you know.' I offered.

'No problem.'

Shelving to the centre of the shop was stacked with folded shirts, meaning: the simplest item to take in number. Calling Woody to the display of suits at one corner of the shop let Paddy know his next move. 'Hi man; Andy you say your name was. These suits Andy...they dark blue or black? It's hard to tell in this light.'

'Yes sir. We've had customers mention this with other garments. The light in here certainly confuses any subtle change in colour. These two suits are in fact dark-blue; a 60/40, wool, polyester mix. An ideal lightweight travel suit; if I may say so sir.'

'Easy washing instructions, as in home clean or dry clean like most formal attire?' I responded.

'Oh, dry clean definitely. Like most suits sir.'

'Do you have a 38 inch regular jacket and 30 inch waist pants?'

'Should be no problem sir; these are new stock, received only yesterday.'

So hyped up and in the zone, on a daily basis, I'd shed half a stone and an inch or two from my taught frame since being in London. Stalling for time, a glance toward Paddy told me he was stacked and packed – his turn to start Yank yapping. If we'd come in separately he could've departed soon as he'd brimmed-up, but we'd entered as a hungry pair and we'd leave as a full pair.

Paddy talked shop in cowboy twang. Like me, he'd studied 'O'level JR Ewing from the Dallas series of options. Unlike local Cockney, he had the impersonation to a tee. It was like watching a TV star impressionist live inside the shop. If I was your average Mike Yarwood from the seventies, Paddy was the blob-on Rory Brenner of the nineties. We'd play about with voices and mannerisms on site and while travelling to work on the tube, Paddy doing Memphis Elvis, turned up lip included, with me, Neil Kinnock, the Welsh Labour party leader laying into the Tories at the Commons. Some passengers were entertained, while others threw you an impersonal glance that told you, 'Shush, fool, I'm trying to read my morning paper'. Packed tube carriages of a morning, what can I say?

Telling Woody I'd carry on looking, as the dark blue suits were not what I wanted, Paddy instantly guided him across the floor for a lifters stroll – time to start binning! I could hear Memphis Elvis. 'Well, well, well, Andy, I wander if you could tell me about shoe size. I think these shoes in a nine seem slightly bigger than my American nine.'

Moving aside the shoe display, he let Andy take over. 'You'll probably need a half-size up. Usually an American nine is the equivalent to a size eight and a half in the UK. Here, try this ten for starters, see how they feel.'

Watching them converse, I rolled four pair of black cotton pants till they were a tight, chip shop bundle. Looking directly at the distracted Woody as he spoke let me gently guide the lump of linen deep into my sown-in-bin. There, there; snug-as. Letting go, I picked up a folded shirt from a pile yet to be tampered with. Unfolding the shirt, I pretended it wasn't quite what I was looking for. Shoving it back in its unfolded state, I purposefully made a mess, unravelling more shirts, then, some nearby sleeveless sweaters.

With everything feeling comfortable, I edged towards lifting more garments. Checking to Andy and Paddy looked green light to me. Rolling-up another two pair of pants, hanger's an'all, I pushed them deep into my armpit on the opposite side of the coat. Lifting ledger: The reason for making a mess was so Woody Andy's concentration remained centered on fixing the shirt display, thus making him less likely to centre-in on two cagily departing Americans. You don't leave a mess at any display places you've taken items from. Keep those racks neat, tidy and out-of-eye. Any shelves or rails showing a noticeable decrease in stock may easily arouse eye contact, a little confusion, followed by suspicion.

'You Ok sir; do you require a little more help with something?' Andy was back.

'No, no problem; I'm gonna carry on looking till something jumps out at me.'

'Ah! I get your drift sir; message understood.'

Andy – quick off the mark – started folding ruffled shirts lying about the display. Having an assistant fold and tidy behind you can make you feel uncomfortable. Me, more than most! As he folded away at the counter, I motioned it was time we were off. As I did, Paddy was in the process of binning more shirts. Showing a high five, I let him finish his business. Once calm and comfortable, he winked the wink of a cool skedaddle. The only thing left before hitting the street was to acknowledge Andy's help. The man had been cool himself. I offered gratitude. 'Thanks for your help Andy. We're gonna carry on up the road for now, but we may well call back before you close. Bye for now.'

'Yes, no problem sir; do call back and see us. Goodbye for now.'

Blinding sunlight and a wide expanse of road meant I struggled to frame Boney. The view came back, busy, busy, busy! Concentrating on catching an Aborigine with a blue Adidas sports bag tuned my scope. He sat across the road roughly fifty yards down. In focus, I noticed his frame outlined by a small patch of grass. I let Paddy know the direction he was in. Closer, I noticed he was nonchalantly studying the form inside the Racing Post. Again, he'd been given clear instruction to watch the shop door by keeping Dixie, and to be on alert for any passing officers of the law. Pulling alongside, Boney hesitantly climbed to his feet. 'Everything's err…custy! I glanced over as you walked out the door.'

Paddy and Boney began arguing; more seriously than usual. 'Have you been keeping an eye on the street, or what?

You've been getting stuck into those horses again haven't yer'?'

'No, I was clocking the street and door.'

'You sure?'

'Yeah, I'm not daft yer' know!'

'Don't know about that?'

'Cheeky cunt!' Answered Boney

'Alright fergerrit; come on, let's go!'

Traipsing away from the under-staffed Next shop, it dawned how keen to earn we'd become. With this new gaff being on the doorstep of the building site it would be hard not to re-enter. If we did, Andy might wonder why the good ol' Dallas boys were still in town.

The path we took around Central London, especially the City area, could be seriously hit and miss, determined by lifters luck. Darting down a back-alley to offload gear, we might end up doing a complete circle, only realizing when a historical monument or landmark showed up. Concentrating on not being tailed by Jacks (plain-clothes police), Floor-walkers (store-detectives), Bizzies (normal police) or nosey Joe public, could render time and place irrelevant – a complete haze. Only when switch-off arrived could you take stock of where you'd been and time elapsed. Obvious streets like Thread needle, Cannon, Fleet and Gresham were soon etched into our City of London mental map.

Buildings like the Bank of England, Fleet Street news offices and St. Paul's Cathedral (where we constantly blessed ourselves when passing) became lifting patrol landmarks and pointers for close-at-hand clobber emporiums. Funny, the guilt you felt whenever you blimped St. Paul's with swag filled pockets. Half-heartedly I tried to avoid the place of worship on more than one occasion and, though we used to bless ourselves with the Catholic sign of the cross, I didn't realise till later it could well have been a Protestant or Methodist church. Seeing as the Royals and a lot of other Big Wigs had ceremonies there, I think our catholic gesture would've been viewed quite cynically by St. Paul's passing congregation. Oh well, thought was there.

'Mickey, where to lad?' Beamed Boney.

'C'mon, jump this bus towards Fleet Street. Remember that designer shop past St. Paul's?'

'Not really.'

'C'mon; you'll know when yer' get there.'

Boarding the bus a few stops wasn't only a good way of spotting new shopping outlets, it was also A1 for offloading gear to the swagbag. Pulling garments from my inside bin, I noted from the urgency in Paddy and Boney's voices they were in serious need of earners; no surprise, being Monday, the day they were always bleeding skint!

Meanwhile, busy clocking the suits too-ing and fro-ing from the warmth of my window seat, I'm wondering if any of them led as dodgy an existence as us. I thought not at that exact moment. Higher earners – yes – day to day dodgy – No. Bigger fiddler's – yes! Minor details caused us to miss our stop. I sprang to my feet, 'Quick, c'mon, quick, jump off here! Up this Street, I know a boss little designer shop up this way.'

I wanted switch-off and back to McRents for the night, but Paddy and Boney were relying on me for another hour or so. Sometimes, Monday, my heart wasn't in it. Usually because I'd been to Barclay's to put something away for a rainy day. Big Time Charlie – now bearing four figured fruit – felt good, but missing the Bank today and carrying a fat wedge made me less hungry than the others.

'Boney, here's yer' big chance boy! D'yer' fancy going in with Paddy? I'll stay outside with the bag if yer' want?'

'Fuck that for a lark! He's clueless Mickey, he'll get us nicked!'

'Listen to Paddy Gambino, Scouse Mafia boss! I'll get us nicked? The only thing that'll get us nicked is one of your daft accents!'

'Well, what accent are you gonna do ay...soft-shite? I

suppose yer' just wanna bounce in with yer' big silly Scouse accent, don't yer'?'

'Shut up! I've been practising me posh English voice all week!'

Soon as Boney mentioned voices the bickering stopped, and laughter began. Paddy and I glanced at Boney, then at each other, and erupted into fits. Killing to keep a straight face, because *this* we really must see, I spluttered, 'Stop it Paddy, I think Boney could do a posh voice easily.'

Paddy straightened up. 'Yer' kidding, there's no way!'

'No I'm not. Go on Bone, show him.'

'Just like that!'

'Shut the fuck up Tommy Cooper and get on with it!'

Squeezing air up my nose and down lungs, I urged Paddy not to laugh. Circling my lips, I threw silent *No's* his way. Swivelling my head side to side, I made the *no* motion over and over. Hoping Boney, encouraged by silence, would bring his new impersonation to proceedings, we waited. Paddy, grasping my thought, swallowed huge gulps of air. Watching him struggle became rib-tickling itself. Boney perked up. 'I can't do it...not right here...now?'

I put him on the spot. 'Forget it then. If yer' can't perform a daft voice in front of us how d'yer' expect shop-staff to play along while Paddy's getting a fill?'

'But you just said, go on Boney, go in with Paddy. Why say that?'

'Testing, to see if you were up for it? But, if yer' can't change yer' accent, it's not worth it is it?'

Paddy continued. 'He's right Boney lad, if they hear the Scouse twang on *you*, we'll be lashed out empty handed inside a minute!'

'I know what yer' saying, but if I go in the shop I'll use me posh accent naturally, when I need to.'

I motioned to go in. 'Nah Bone...doesn't work like that. If yer' don't do it now that's the end of it. I'll go in.'

'Ok! Ok! Agh Fuck it! Here yer' go. Err...what can I say then?'

'Just pretend yer' from Windsor...like that Princess Anne bird who gave you'se a lift the other day. Yer' know, something posh; something like: *I'm off to a wedding at the weekend; a jolly good bash indeed. I'm thinking loose and comfortable please young man; nothing too starched that may hinder a good waltz.'*

'Yer' kidding! That's some mouthful that!' He offered.

'Come on Paddy, let's go in. Boney, just wait by that building so we know whereabouts you...'

'Alright, alright, I'll say it! Listen, I'll just say the bit about the wedding, Ok?'

'Yeah, go on then, that'll do.'

Taking a deep breath he spoke in slow motion. 'I'm orff tew are wedding at the weeeekend and a jollerrr...'

We never heard the rest, we were in absolute stitches. Laughing out loud, passers-by had a gander. It didn't matter, we were gone! Things got worse when I stopped for a moment, looked at Boney, and said. 'Go on, get in the shop now!'

'You better stop laughing first...Anyway, why right now?'

'Cos yer' sound like Lurch from the Adams family getting strangled by Uncle Fester in a fight!'

Through laughter I heard Boney going, 'Why get in the shop now, why now ay?'

'Get in there Lurch. You'll scare the staff onto the street with that voice. Quick, get in, me and Paddy'll empty the shelves!'

Paddy was creased. Every time I looked at him, with Boney gawping sent me over the edge as coaster waves of convulsion hit home. It was a belly laugh of internal damage proportions. Hitting a crescendo, getting scary, it calmed for seconds, before erupting again. People walking in and out of Fleet Street offices smiled at us like we were story-happy Reporters who'd hit the headline jackpot.

Struggling to stand, each time we came to our senses, there was Boney, arms folded, looking perplexed and all alone in the world. Cramped in a heap on the pavement, an approaching Copper with penny slot eyes, scowling face to the fore, gave us the ol' once-over. I took his look as: *let me find something to arrest you for.* Paranoid or what? Dusting down, trying not to stare, I muttered, 'Get yer' act together, Officer Killjoy on the beat!'

'Yer' only right! Miserable looking bastard's walking like he's gorra truncheon stuck up his arse!'

'At least he's shut you'se two up.' Boney quipped.

Glancing at the strong arm of misery, instruction was needed. I offered some. 'Follow *me,* this way, come on. He'll be asking for a look in the swagbag if we hang around any longer.'

I looked for an underground sign. Whenever switch-off approached or Plod patrolled in proximity, knowing tube Station's lay all along the Central City line at St. Paul's, Chancery Lane and the Bank, gave the feeling a good escape route was always at hand; knowing which one to head to was another story. Edging to get beyond Officer Killjoy range, headed in a Northerly direction, we aimed east towards St. Paul's the conscience twanger where a tube station glimmered beneath its dome.

Walking to the cathedral Paddy tugged me, stating another few quid wouldn't go amiss. Catching sight of the mighty white dome Christopher Wren designed so people like me kept conscience in check, I felt for the fat wedge of Queen Lizzie's and realized switch-off time had arrived. Looking at the crucifix sitting atop of the dome confirmed my thoughts. I'm convinced Wren designed it so anyone treading a crooked path in Central London would contemplate a u-turn to the straight and narrow on sight.

'Paddy, come on lad, let's spew it.'

'Ah, just one more bit of graft ay Mickey?'

I tried another approach. 'England versus the Argies tomorrow, it's the big quarter-final!'

'And since when have you been arsed about England in the World Cup?'

'I'm not really I just wanna see the game.'

Boney butted in, 'I've had a bet on it. But who cares about that now?'

Putting them off got me nowhere. 'Forget it! Come on, let's get in here.'

Being keen to get inside, Boney missed Bagman instruction. The three of us waltzed inside. A small suit and tie affair... with nobody in attendance; we looked at each other. No one spoke. I pointed to expensive looking suits. We made our way over. Still nobody showed.

Clocking the till area I noticed an open leather suitcase lying against a wall. Gliding over, expectant of staff interruption, I let the other two go about their business. I could hear people arguing somewhere behind a half-open door. It led to a back room within the premises. It sounded heated. Swallowing, I blimped red and green cash bags inside the case...I was on one. Lifting the suitcase in both arms it clicked shut. Turning towards the door, Paddy and Boney were busy rolling and loading suits into coats. I got their attention, 'Ay – move it – now!'

Paddy looked at me, then the rack. 'Fuck it!

Taking four more suits, he rolled them into a large bundle and stuffed them under his arm. Arms full, I kept the door open with my foot. He was the last one out. Walking across the open concourse I struggled to stuff the case into Boneys swagbag. Carrying on through a subway-type tunnel, we hailed a Taxi. A mile or two up the road we paid the driver a few pounds and jumped from his cab. Walking directly into Bank tube station, and now becoming a habit, I paid three full fares to Gants Hill.

I tried to view the contents of the case. It wouldn't open. Exiting at destination, we jumped another cab to the door of

McRents; making it the fastest time ever for that Eastbound homeward journey. Funny thing, we hardly spoke. Excitement, or hope in our hearts? Whatever? It stopped us gabbing. Seemed we were getting used to earning, illegality and getaways.

Opening the door to my Coop, gear rained onto the bed from all angles. Pulling the case from the swagbag, formal threads got ignored. Prizing the lock came easily now we had space and comfort. Nestled inside, the green and red cash bags looked snug. I started dealing them out. Eventually we counted just over £27,000. Christmas had come real early in bedsit land.

Once the hoo-ha of having decent dough died down and England had been Diego hand-balled out of the World Cup, regarding cash flow, everything just fell into place. Earners were an everyday occurrence; honest work, an absolute hindrance. It was as though opening the lock on the briefcase had opened a window to a world of bigger, illegal opportunity; like we'd freed ourselves from chains of guilt, worry and turmoil.

Inner London, fast running out of High streets and new premises to visit, meant travel distance and lifting range expanded. Drivers were hired. Household items like expensive cutlery, kitchenware and bathroom sets were all part of the Hoisting menu. Leather bags, wallets and cameras had started slipping up sleeves and inside coats on a daily basis; while ornaments, clocks and wall pictures we couldn't sell, adorned the walls and window sills of three cramped bedsits (Clifford the Rasta had moved out, Paddy moved in). Hamish McRent started calling the Chicken Coops, the House of Scouse, and seemed happy to have us as tenants since we'd re-painted and tidied the bedsits beyond recognition; with his tight-arsed approval of course.

Earning fantastic money and saving like a stock exchange Jew-boy on a business buying hitlist, I bunce-buzzed! The fact we were paying for hardly anything – still cash-in-hand 9-5, with the Social paying the rent – we had money to burn and, that's exactly what the other two were doing! The government of the day seemed happy to leave you hidden away, signing on, while the tax-avoiding Southern entrepreneurs of the building trade were more than happy to pay illegal workers like ourselves in nice, cold, invisible cash. We called it the ancient Chinese proverb of 'No cards-in, mean no find-out!'

Weekends we travelled as far as Brighton in the South, Dover and Margate in the East, Norwich and Kings Lynn in the North and Oxford, Reading and Swindon in the West. For those jaunt's we now had wheels, ably supplied by Vinny, with Left Foot Lenny, fiery faced Birdsegg, or, to a lesser degree, one of Vinny's son's as willing jockey. As for Birdsegg, he was road rage personified long before it hit the modern motorway syllabus. We were a gang and we were earning. No more than ten people off-site knew our game, but virtually the whole on-site workforce did and, Friday without fail, they were ready and waiting to buy. We had orders for irons, kettles, curtains, bedding, sports goods, birthday presents; the list was endless. We had a few scary moments, but suited and booted with scrapes par for the course, things were running smooth as a well-varnished rocking horse. Money slapped conscience bang in the face, when even Sunday became an earning day; if anywhere was open and up for lifting grabs.

A positive thing that came from a close scrape was you learned what *not* to do. Wise people made mistakes before rectifying a situation. Boney, never about to apply that law, meant the gambling Aborigine stayed outdoors almost continuously. I knew, law of averages, it couldn't last, but we had a far greater chance of earning and staying free while he stayed out on the street. Paddy and I tinkered with the idea of paying him to stay in work during the week, or at home during the weekend, which sounds crazy, but we contemplated it nonetheless.

Having money, meant travelling about with money, and a

major lifting lesson learned early was to carry enough readies
in pocket to pay for anything you might walk out with. This
was sometimes impossible, like when we walked out of a Bond
Street gallery with 3 paintings worth roughly a grand each,
which we sold for £150 apiece. As that antiques fella with the
orange face would say, '*cheap as chips!*' The more expensive or
exclusive an item, the more you'd be bargained down and, less
likely you'd have the readies to front a storekeeper if they
became dubious about reasons for entry. This happened to
me in Cambridge one Saturday afternoon when I de-tagged a
leather jacket and wrongly made tracks to the exit door.

I blame my mistake on the music being played. Making me
impatient to leave that miserable *Lady in Red* song played on
the radio. Quick staff-check came back all green light, till I hit
the street and a final glance through the window told me
Chaka Khan, the hugely bosomed female staff, stood holding
the wire I'd just cut while counting the leather jackets on
display – minus one, of course!

Moving through traffic, she came steaming out of the
doorway, her tits pushing cars out of the way. She was already
sweating when I fronted her in a department store doorway.
Without noise or fuss, she looked at me, I looked at her, she
said straight and true, '£139 please.' She'd seen me hovering
about the coat display, but not seen the wire cutters or the rest
of the crew. It didn't matter, I didn't argue the toss. The shop-
diva, though sweating, typified cool. Above her heaving
bosom she had eyes that burned a hole in you. At that moment
they laser'ed in on me. I looked at Madame Medusa, for about
two seconds longer than I should've, and muttered, 'Right you
are gorgeous' and stumped up £150 before I turned to stone.

'I hope you're not expecting change?' She offered.

'Of course not sweetheart; I'm sorry about that.'

'You've got some front haven't you?'

'Nowhere near as nice as yours though.'

She looked down at her fabulous kitchen shelf and

nervously laughed. It was time for me to disappear before she changed tact, a passing shopper got involved, or Officer shop-patrol turned up. Walking away, I told her she was beautiful; she giggled some more. My god! I felt like going back so she could make me rock-solid. Of course, I never did. It was a lucky escape. When I got back to where the motor was parked – half a mile from town – the others struggled with my story, so I dropped it forthwith. *Lucky, lucky, lucky* I'm thinking, on the drive back to London. The other two, tone deaf to my humming the tune about saving or carrying money, made me want to give up on monetary moral instruction…if you could call it that?

I was able to spend freely, without indulgence. Never being one for material possessions or addictions, whatever they may be, when it came to financial freedom and being able to breathe easy, I was as driven and motivated as any gullible addict. Continuing to give subs to Boney and Paddy, they continued to pay me back, but I had bigger plans and, though I never said *no*, it bugged me no end. Boney's bets got bigger as Paddy's female acquaintances grew in number. I mean, he was even shagging two 40'ish plus housewives – Julie Christie and Jane Fonda – one next-door and one further up the road in Chicken Coop County. Visiting the same brass on a regular basis, nearby in Illford, they ribbed me I was in love. They couldn't get their heads around me helping myself when I needed to, whereas they remained helpless in their need to. Big difference that one.

One night, Vinny introduced us to one of his sisters who'd been selling our knock-off swag for the past few months. We hit it off immediately and I ended up seeing her behind everyone's back. The reason we were secretive came down to me going on about not mixing business with pleasure, like Paddy chatting-up tasty store girls, Boney paying gambling debts with shoplifted goods his bookie had ordered, or the same with anyone he'd lost a bet to. Yeah, that and the fact Vinny's sister,

Anna had a rowdy looking husband and two kids.

Her husband worked shifts as a train driver on the London underground, and sold stuff we'd Hoisted on a regular basis. Meanwhile, we visited some of the West End's finer hotels on our own basis. I felt guilty when I thought he could be rumbling the train underneath a hotel we'd be visiting, while I'd be rumbling the bed above. It was in, out, then over and out after a few months; one of those instant attractions, not a case of me or her out on the hunt. Instead of becoming more easy-going, due to wedge-on-hip, I was becoming more ruthless in most aspects of life. I could see an opportunity – an opening – and was not prepared to go back to dole-drums for no one.

Paddy and Boneys need for extra earners remained insatiable, due to not giving a square of Dairy Milk about future rainy days; resulting in: they were up for Hoisting duty even more than I was. Suddenly, where there had been no conflict, a difference in needs and wants arose and the two of them hit the shops together. They had mentioned it in passing conversation but I thought it was Hoisting bluster. I only found out in work when Vinny told me they'd brought extra goods to his home the previous night. Asking why I hadn't been there, I blurted some stupid excuse as I'd been dabbling with his sister.

I found out the two of them had visited the West End and earned a few quid, and they'd said 'Keep this stuff separate from the other gear.' For some reason I didn't object and part of me knew they'd come unstuck; probably the constantly lending money part. But, like I knew Paddy's one pair of eyes on Boney simply wasn't enough, I also knew they'd never listen.

Week later, same scenario, they're out on the pavement again and the ol' dreaded knock arrives at McRents. I'd gone to sleep after having a few drinks with the Salford Spanner in the communal kitchen, before being woken abruptly by someone banging at my bedsit door. Paddy and Boney went on to tell me how they'd been chased and caught outside Harrods with the swagbag in tow. Paddy, as I knew he would, blamed Boney, and Boney, well...he just mumbled his usual bag-of-shite about how it wasn't his fault.

Floorwalkers had heard them speaking after a small French boy, on holiday with his mother, alerted her that Boney had put stuff inside his coat. The wise-arse Floorwalkers kept distance, once shop-staff informed them what the French kid told his mum. While in the lift they'd used their own accent, enough for listening security to give them a tug. They told arresting officers they were day-tripping from Liverpool. Their families confirmed this, after previously been given the half-truth about identifying us as still living at home, if something untoward happened due us to dole fiddling at McRents. They were charged and bailed. If our families in the North had known the full SP they'd have blown our shoplifting shelter straight out the River Thames with that old cherub!

In one aspect it was a close escape. If London Plod had bailed into the Chicken Coops, chances were the three of us would've bailed straight into Wormwood Scrubs without passing Go! Hastily taking stock of goods on offer in the three rooms, we came up with roughly twenty to thirty grinds worth of knock-off swag; mostly and, stupidly, still price-tagged. Though easier to sell gear tagged, price tags simplified an officer's task-in-hand to trace and identify what to charge you with. It was another lesson we'd known about, but been lazy carrying out. Not from then on, for me, that is. Incredibly, the two of them had kept most of the cash from the briefcase under the floorboards under the bed. After showing me cash bundles, and green and red bags I'd told Boney to destroy, I knew it was a total waste of time trying to educate or advise.

Few weeks later, with social reports in and Paddy and Boney heading to Bow Street Magistrates, the two of them, mooching in the West End, got nabbed again. This time, Police identification was easy, the process quicker, and jail, just around the corner. It really was that quick! No trips to the Lake District for shoplifting rehabilitation, just plain old Jug. Caught stuffing clobber into the swagbag by an off-duty Police Officer, down a side street near Bond Street tube station, they'd left Browns hooty department store overloaded. Asking what they were up to before revealing his identity, they told him to fuck-off and not to be nosey. Officer Tweed Jacket proceeded to scream to the whole of Oxford Street about what was going on. Members of Joe Public then performed rugby tackles and headlocks, till uniformed Dibble arrived in number. As fresh-air breathers they were over, as a lifting team, we were over and out! It really, really was that quick. One minute: earner's galore. Next minute: jail, and, as Patti Labelle had once sang in Ilford Palais, *on my own.*

MONEY

Soon as Paddy and Boney were busy scrubbing floors inside Wormwood big house, I got busy keeping up appearances at McRents. Signing on in place of Paddy, Spanner did likewise for Boney. This meant that A: Hamish got his rent paid as usual. B: We had keys to two empty entertaining/swag rooms, if the need arose, and C: Existing tenants, who knew Paddy and Boney had gone to jail, wouldn't have to get used to new occupiers who might not be on the wavelength. Miserable tits apart, they were happy the way things were. Though, we never heard much from the denim-clad dyke these days – thank god!

The communal kitchen was brimmed with food, drink and brand new cooking utensils, while air-fresheners, towels and cleaning products were heaped in domestic abundance. The upstairs and downstairs bathrooms held enough shampoo, toothpaste and toothbrushes to last a year. At least the penniless tenants of McRents had one thing to smile about. On High street walkabouts I'd pilfer so many toiletries from chemists like Boots, I'd have to return by taxi due to being weighed down like a hotel cleaner's trolley. I'd have to exit the taxi around the corner from McRents as all kinds of smellies and jellies would be falling from my person. Coat pockets contained twenty tubes of toothpaste, twenty packs of razor blades and ten tins of deodorant. Baggy coat sleeves held twenty toothbrushes, twenty bars of soap, plus other numerous combs, brushes and nail clippers; all waiting to roll down forearms held in by the pinch of a sleeve.

Scribbling Paddy's signature at the Social, I only needed his ID to cash the giro at the Post Office. Nobody at the DHSS took an interest in your appearance, you getting a job, or who the fuck you were! The black economy under Maggie was like a runaway ghost train at the avaricious theme park and, for frontline social security people, it was as though the ride had become unstoppable and they, like everyone else, had long given up the ghost!

Out and about the city streets, riding my own version of that black economy ghost train, I too wanted to capitalize and, same as any pinstriped, pavement-pounding Yuppie, I pushed for a seat on the ride. Back at work, I asked Vinny to get Left Foot Lenny down to the site. He did, next day. Telling Lenny I wanted earners, I asked could we go abroad, before informing Vinny I wouldn't be on the next Brumble job and the few weeks left at this one would be my last. I'd gotten to know the rest of the workforce well enough, but I was earning so much money outside 9 to 5 I wanted room to roam.

In the weeks after Paddy and Boneys derailment I got better and better at mooching independently. I'd been by myself often before, but it was difficult to lug Hoisted gear about while trying to earn. I thought about bringing someone I could trust down from Liverpool, but decided on the unknown Lenny Edwards instead. For someone older than me, Lenny seemed okay. If anything, he was a lot more professional than Paddy and Boney; harbouring future shoe shop dreams of his own helped I suppose.

First weekend, we caught the ferry from Dover to Belgium and, along with a couple of hundred left-footed shoes pilfered inside and outside the shoe shops of Antwerp, Brussels and across the border in Cologne and Düsseldorf, we came back with bundles of designer clothing that included fifteen Cardin suede jackets that sold for £100 apiece. With nobody borrowing from me or distracting my view, life simplified immensely.

Left Foot paid up-front for my part in the shoe-display-days and Vinny, like clockwork, was bang on with the Monday bung. To me, I was raking it in. The Friday following the shoe trip I collected my legal wages from Vinny, before going for a stroll down Museum Street in the Bloomsbury area of London. I had no real intent in mind…okay, ideas about a new Hoisting coat lurked somewhere, but main interest lay in taking a culture stroll before finding a clean café for a nosebag.

Entering a small gallery, I noticed a black and white TV monitor showing four different frames of the shop, with no one in attendance. Looking about, I zipped downstairs to find the basement deserted. Checking some smaller paintings, I was astounded at the price tags. The shop looked scruffy. I presumed it was on leasehold, otherwise, with these prices, surely the owner's would've spent a little on décor if they owned the building outright. I tutted to myself: *minor details, minor details!*

Still nobody showed. An office at one end had an infra red camera above the door frame. Pushing up the collar on my cotton raincoat, it made no real difference to my appearance. Confront any Hoister with a camera and most push a scarf or collar up, or drill head to chest on cue. It's automatic.

Moving toward the office door, a dusty window held a couple of clean spots, telling you it was empty. Ignoring the fact I was in the galleries new home movie, I turned the handle. It creaked open. I entered. It smelled musty and damp. The usual office desk, polished to gleam, held a medium sized oil painting of men in red coats atop horses. It was signed. If it was worth a few quid it wasn't something I knew anything about. Pulling all three drawers together got me nowhere. Slow down cowboy…

Above, loud creaking floorboards zinged at the strings of my heart. The noise, directly above me, with stairs at the other end of the basement, meant I had time. Rummaging through the drawers singly told nothing but pen and pencil stories. No good to me. Shop keeping books heaped about the floor, along with discarded picture frames, made it hard to walk quietly in the cramped space. Floorboards creaked even louder, strangely reminding me of my old school gym – *minor details* – time to go!

If anyone tugged me at the door I'd give it the old 'looking for a toilet' blag. If that didn't work and an in-depth-type owner wanted to investigate further I wouldn't wait about for questioning; especially if a couple of small, pricey pictures were on board. A final scan of the desk told me to check the back of the oil painting for a price. Too big to place inside a coat, curiosity got the better of creak fear. Lifting and turning the picture produced no price tag, but underneath the frame lay a number of brown, sealed envelopes and a small green cashbox. A tiny key protruded from its lock. Bingo! More like it!

I went to turn the key. Another coffin creak from above stopped me. Stuffing the brown envelopes into normal side pockets, I glided the cashbox to my oversize binning pocket. Loose change rattled inside the box, rattling me! Silence being golden it sounded like a fruit machine jackpot. I got thinking: *if no one's heard, at least nosebag's paid for.* Walking upstairs was filled with apprehension in all expectation of a tug. Which proved wasted, when I noticed the owner talking to a prospective purchaser deep inside the arse-end of the premises. Unable to see the scarf-wrapped customer clearly, the owner was 90% Rigsby from Rising Damp; the 10% lacking for look-alike completion: him standing more upright than the actor Leonard Rossiter. They stood in the area above the basement office; the constant creaking no doubt. He glanced towards me. 'See anything you like sir?'

'Yes, I did actually. I'm about to fetch my wife to give it the once over.'

La-di-da Queens English was back on the boil.

'We'll be closing soon sir. Don't be long.'

Not a good thing to say when you're in the business of selling paintings, I'm thinking, instantly followed by: *you're going to be waiting a long time for me squire Rigsby!* Making my way along the pavement, anticipation of monetary-gain drowned any trepidation I'd felt leaving. Labelling the shop Master Rigsby's gallery, accordingly, if sales of paintings, frames and sketches were brisk, it was surely time for a new coat of paint for the business and its owner. *Probably one of those eccentric tight-arses with a large stash under the floorboards…*I'm off again; followed by thoughts of Jack Wilde as the Artful Dodger in the musical of *Oliver*, followed by more *minor bleeding details!* Whatever? Master Rigsby's it was. Hopefully the scruffy art dealer would soon be in a grooming salon while the decorators were in, and not be seeing me in many a moon.

The fine thing about London was once you were gone, you were long gone! It was no one-horse Balamory town like Watford or St. Albans, or any of those other places littered around the M25 where if you copped-good, you had to depart pronto on the first stagecoach out. London – few blocks and you were along with the throng!

Marching like a turtles head was about to escape my backside, the cashbox whacked my knee as it swayed in front side to side. It suddenly felt heavy. Garfunkel's welfare restaurant showed face. With no queue between me and a seat, I entered to sit deep within its bowels. The place was packed – nothing new – but a waitress, clocking the hungry eyes, let me order gammon steak with pineapple, egg and chips, along with a coke, minus the menu. Order placed, the toilets beckoned, as rumbling hunger and the turtles head got drowned by anticipation and a weighty coat. Time to get rid!

Entering the men's bog – which it was – I was hit with a stench that shouted tramps socks, blocked khazi's and parmesan underpants rolled into one! Pushing open the door to the ladies, I was hit by air-freshener, silence and a feint smell of woman wee: a far better environment for opening a prize. Darting in, I pushed open a cubicle door and locked it behind me. Reaching for the cashbox I was loose-change, rattle-wary. Though the toilets were empty anybody could walk in. I didn't care about any 'boy in girl's toilet stories', my only concern was not using the cashbox as a tambourine. Pulling pants down to cover manly brogues, I left my navy boxing shorts up. Placing the cashbox on bare knees, its coldness startled me. Putting wrists to its metallic sides I cooled down. *Slow down cowboy*. Heeding thoughts, I concentrated on the noisy plumbing mechanism, but cashbox hunger kept interrupting...

After a little cat and mouse with myself I eventually turned the key and lifted the lid. Small compartments inside were filled with loose change. My immediate reaction was one of disappointment, till I lifted out the loose plastic compartment to reveal a number of tightly banded notes. Showing fifties on the outsides, I hissed a Yessss! Get paid! Eagerly, but quietly as possible, I counted the bundles. Running fingers through each second bundle like a dealer with new packs of cards, I counted fourteen banded stacks of crisp, brand new fifties and one which contained only tens and twenties. Only tens and twenties – Ha! Laughable, I know!

The tens and twenties bundle was the only one strapped together by an elastic band. It said £750 in deep blue ink on the top note. Roughly half the fifty stacks were banded with a cellophane strip that said £2500. Quick estimation told me I could be holding 35 grand. My brain turned low light cool to full boil hot! Wanting to scream to the heavens, I hissed another Yessss...stopped in its tracks by the noise of the entrance door opening and the click of stilettos entering the cubicle next to mine. Pushing pants inside out, further over brogues, it was time to hold breath and wait.

The rustle of skirt and underwear being dropped tempted me to look underneath. The thought of fifty pound notes compared to a squatting pensioner wearing baggy, piss-stained drawers, and I resisted with ease. As the lady started to pee the entrance door to the toilets opened again, and again, and again. Women nattered freely. One said to another, 'Yes I'm queuing.' More women entered. I couldn't wait anymore. Slowly lifting the cashbox from my knees, I turned and locked its tiny key. Placing it into my inside pocket, I deftly pulled up trousers, tucked in my shirt, fastened every-thing together, pulled the chain, coughed once and exited the cubicle.

In the confined space the huddle of women looked startled. Eyeing me suspiciously, one young lady giggled. There were five women waiting. Muttering something about blocked toilets next door, I exited without looking back. Walking towards my seat, I took a huge gulp of coke the waitress had left at my table and skedaddled out onto the street to jump the tube at Bond Street back to McRents.

That evening I counted out almost £36,000. The ego part of me wanted to go out and get drunk. I felt rich. The wise part didn't want to dull hyper-senses for one second, or lose sight of my new bundle of bunce. The door to my Chicken Coop looked vulnerable and cardboard-thin. It dawned that in the space of a few months I'd gone from being a boy with biscuit crumb pockets on the Dock Road of Liverpool, to a lad with a breezeblock of cash on the streets of London. Again, I felt rich. I thought about whether I was rich?

Liking the feeling of being wedged with cash, I ended up sitting in watching a dodgy pirate video of Al Pacino starring as Tony Montana in Scarface. I'd seen it maybe ten times. The fella in the movie had his own sleazy American dream, which typically ended in the usual drug-nut-gangster, loose-the-plot scenario. It was a bit unbelievable at times: too much money, too fast, with too many Tommy-guns involved. But, I got the message about not losing the plot when you catch sight of Disneyland. I felt rich over and over again. Bedsit vulnerability and thoughts of Boney 'bigging us up' inside jail, meant an uneasy night's sleep went pretty much like my first night in bedsit land. But, instead of job worries, woken moments were spent thinking: *It's a nap I'm going the same place but, at least no more returning home demoralized with trousers around ankles again!*

All weekend I deliberated on what to do with the money. Taking in a movie in Leicester Square before heading back east to walk Cranbrook Park endlessly, gave no respite. I was scared of taking such a large amount to the bank and, laughable though it seems, the rules of the Social said you couldn't have more than £2000 in savings if you wanted to carry on receiving benefit. No way did I want to be thrown off the Social. Signing on had reached the stage where it wasn't about picking up the paltry money, it was all about holding on to your identity as a no-mark – a loser! While you were a non-achieving, welfare dreg the authorities had you in check, knew who you were, whereabouts you were at and remained utterly disinterested!

Vinny and his missus reckoned I should buy a house, seeing as they had a fella who could sort me a no-questions mortgage. So, after viewing a couple of humble drums with Vinny as overseer in tow, that's what I did. I didn't move in, that was way too suspicious. The place was put with a property management company, given a quick scrub and paint by Vinny and me, before being let to a tenant immediately. The Estate agent who sold me the house had apparently been buying heaps of formal attire from the lining of my coat for months now; something he was made aware of during selling procedures. They're always up for making and saving a few bob those men of dwelling selling. While my fees were lowered, the mortgage and insurance company footed the bill. I was a homeowner – a contender ma! Up and sprinting, I had a stake in Thatcher's Blighty.

A Financial advisor-come-gangster also convinced me about some share issue, making me an investor too. Moving about all over the place, not wanting to stop, my ears and feet were tingling. Word travels fast underneath the underbelly and soon a few 'do you wanna be in my gang' types showed face. Never interested in all that comrade robbers and earning for the gang boss malarkey, one thing that did open me up a little was a phone call to Vinny from Left Foot asking if I might be up for a stateside shopping visit. Another continent on the mind broadening map sounded about right. Besides putting me right off the underbelly radar, it was time to visit the biggest consumer society on earth: New York, clobberville, USA.

Lenny had an Irish cousin connected to the Westies: a rowdy, Irish-American gang from the Hell's Kitchen area of New York. His Westie cousin named, unoriginally, Seamus, reckoned greenbacks were available for the right operators in and around New York and the Eastern seaboard area. Lenny thought he and I were potential operators who might well fit the Hoisting dollar bill!

My London lifting round, becoming a little jaded after entering the same well-paying premises too often, meant a change of Hoisting environment made a lot of short-term sense. I'd noticed a number of shop staff giving me overly long shopkeeper's bleeper's – the lingering eye! Changing route for a while, most London shops, on return, would be manned by new faces. Staff turnaround in booming 80's London was revolving door employment, and probably a right pain in the arse for store owners. Some shops became Ace-Face places overnight; and whereas some hip, young staff member might be killing to work in the new 'show-face-in-place' for groovy reasons, I'd be wanting an *in* laced with almost opposite intentions. Yeah, I wanted the fashionable gear on offer too – selling purposes mind you – but, once inside, I wanted nobody noticing my shifty features doing the groovy rounds, and *incognito* remained one of the ten commandments of any lifting day. Etched into my lifting ledger and brain, they roughly read:

1. Clean shaven, dress smart looking the part at all times (carry filofax, empty wallet).
2. No Liverpool or hard street accents. Touristy lingo and posh accents at all times.
3. Treat shop staff with respect and manners, even if they're idiots.
4. No ten gallon hats. In other words: don't draw attention in any way. Be discreet.
5. Park vehicle far away as possible from 'scene of crime' and never return to it.
6. Carry no bags or identifying traits…change appearance regularly (glasses etc).
7. Carry enough money to be able to pay on the spot.
8. Least discourse as possible with staff. Leave no lasting impression. Don't eyeball.
9. Remove price tags immediately and any traceable signs on goods.
10. Never leave a shop or premises in a hurry, or if you've been spotted carrying.

Catching a direct flight from Heathrow, Lenny and I landed in New York stocked to the brim with posh fragrances taken from Airport duty free shops. My oversized sleeves bulged with expensive pure perfumes like Chanel no.5, while cartons of Embassy cigarettes and King Edward cigars lined the bottom and back of my raincoat. Same as clobber parcels, you'd only notice the bulges if you were acting like Inspector Hoover Nostrils, close-up wearing x-ray specs. Before boarding, to be on the safe and comfy side, goods were offloaded into a tasty little Samsonite I'd hand-balled from a luggage shop. Briefcases were the exception to the bag rule, and were often handy and could look the part in formal wear shops.

Arriving in New York we were met by the outstretched arms of Seamus, sporting a mild resemblance to U2 singer, Bono. It could have been the black leather jacket and black jeans tucked into high leg army boots that sent me that way. Closer inspection showed a Morris dancer's, maypole mullet (short sides, long, flowing locks at the back), adding to the overall Bono impression. U2 it was. Leaving the airport, I was buzzing! Like any wanderlust warrior I'd always wanted to taste the Big Apple. First impressions told me we were in the overgrown, cooking apple variety of all cities, with the place heaving, bouncing and intertwining like a lice-riddled head at all times.

Seamus guided us to his car, a clapped out, rusty, old Buick. Momentarily free from traffic, Seamus' guided tour's was in town. The fella, peat-mining-Paddy up-front, spoke full-on, nasal New Yoyk American. Before bags were wearily downed at his Westside flat, he'd driven us on a mad, two hour tour of the city. Turnpikes, Avenues and Highways were rumbled over, under and across. No questions about jetlag or whether we were hungry were offered, and Seamus – king of the Irish-American blarney – made everything sound so interesting that Lenny and I hardly spoke. Passing the iconic Chrysler building, he jammed the brakes, jumped from the car and dashed into a Deli. Returning in an instant with a bag full of drinks, bagels and yucky Hershey's chocolate, the fella seemed electric: yeah, the electric Yankee Bono. I liked him already.

Days after we'd settled into a room each at Seamus' flat, and brief lifting tours of New York, Manhattan and Brooklyn had been undertaken, we started to get out beyond New York's swell to the countrified golf courses of the eastern states. Seamus, golf course and mall maps constantly at the ready, was a brilliant guide, great company and an A1 lifting jockey. Not only did he do as he was told, as in: park in the right spot, remain alert for uniforms and stay incognito, he also came up with a few bright Hoisting ideas himself. Trying to get us to eat Hershey's chocolate and sour tasting American candy definitely wasn't one of them. Sustenance and stimulant to march the mall or roam the golf courses meant sickly doughnuts replaced gorgeous Cadbury's; till I found Baby Ruth chocolate bars.

One better idea of Seamus' was hitting course golf shops at the crack of dawn – dressed like Arnold Palmer of course – though I drew a line when Left Foot said we should also don plus fours and checked, Ronny Corbett jumpers. Whereas most High Street clobber emporiums, strip malls or shopping malls didn't open their doors till 8, 9 or even 10 o'clock, most course pro-shops opened the minute the eagle hovered and the cock crowed. Amateur and pro-golfers, along with early rise businessmen were normally catered for by a fully-open though sparsely staffed golf shop, situated at the clubhouse entrance or 1st tee to almost every course. The more up-market the greenery, the fancier the golf apparel on offer.

Edging towards the more gentrified joints, for obvious expensive clobber reasons, even basic caddy shops sold a decent set of clubs. Nobody, and I mean not a six-inch hot-dog sausage on those North American courses, suspected they had golf playing Hoisters in their midst at 6:30 in the morning. And, if we'd cleaned-up real early, sometimes the next course on the map might see us take in nine holes or so. Me, a golfer – Ha! Jack Nicklaus in a baggy mac? More like out of place Northern Urchin with itchy fingers!

Soon we were walking in munching doughnuts with a brief good morning, before walking out with the most expensive clubs in tow. Some were dispatched via Newark Airport by post to Vinny in London, while most were sold by a well known Westside fence Seamus had grown up with along the banks of the Hudson. Once mid-morning arrived and we'd visited three or four courses, it was time for normal business to begin. If we'd earned well and a round of golf didn't entice, and top-of-the-range individual clubs, sets and clothing were sat inside the trunk...sorry, the boot of whatever tasty car we'd hired (you couldn't drive about in Seamus' cop-magnet Buick, especially on course) then come nine/ten o'clock we were putting for home.

At switch-off time we'd pull in at tourist info spots to check for posh, five star hotels and visit their well-stocked in-house shops. Too far astray from New York, we'd stay the night in lavish three-bedded rooms. It seemed a lot cheaper than England, especially London, but it still took a while to sink in that it was *me* sleeping off hangovers in luxurious five star residences. A lot of the opulently grand, fancier places contained their own golf shop, and I'd be up and down like a yoyo using the lift to lift. First visit to the States, I loved the gaff so much I stayed for two months.

Like Central London, the further from inner city New York, Philadelphia or Boston in the North, the easier Hoisting to be found. Seamus told us how difficult it would be to lift at Macy's, Saks and Fifth Avenue, but compared to places like Liverpool, Leeds and Manchester it was a complete and utter doddle!

We were in the land of plenty, including plenty of floor-walking security who, in the land of epic movie making, were not the greatest aisle actors: more Arnold Schwarzenegger, plain clothes than, say, British Daniel Day Lewis's. Ok, I'm stretching it with the Danny Day's, but for shop Oscars – forget it! Not on the Hoist everyday, as in London, New York had about everything you wanted, whenever you wanted it. I wanted to get a driving license. After a few lessons and a quick read-up, I passed the driving test with ease. Unlike the British driving test, the American one, like the department stores, was a doddle!

Some mornings, same as back home, I'd take long walks through the city's tourist hotspots: Greenwich Village, and

Central and Battery Park; its miles and miles of piers, bridges and Dockland working waterfront, and the hard-nosed, immigrant littered streets of Harlem, Little Italy and Brooklyn. For mooching and travelling, I'd clued-up on dressing the part whatever the stage. On American golf courses: preppy, cashmere sweaters and polo tops, like a young, freshman, Jack Nicklaus with altar boy manners. In shops: camera and phoney credit card on show, like a daft $500 a day tourist, speaking more country bumpkin, John Voight than street hustler, Dustin Hoffman in Midnight Cowboy. Traipsing mean streets: myself, Mickey Mac, a designer inclined, ladder climbing, rag-arsed urchin!

Getting to know a few Westside drinking buddies...sorry, mates, it was almost a drag to fly home. Left Foot, being married, flew home three times within that first two months. Not happy about having to carry the un-posted heaps of swag we wanted Vinny to sell, a first class ticket eased his burden while also making the flight attendants ease- off on baggage allowance. Pub crawling New York's Irish bars with Seamus' tightly knit crew, I bumped into a beautiful young Columbian girl called Rosa one night at a Shamrock swallee in Yonkers. We'd meet in Central Park, near the Dakota buildings where John Lennon had been shot, before walking, talking and visiting her basic apartment for some basic but beautiful loving. Where and why do those hot, Hispanic ladies get those marvellous bottom cheeks? The one thing that could make me forget about Fifth Avenue fashion houses was Rosa's sweet, sweet hourglass figure. Girl was seriously tidy I tell you!

Getting to the meeting point early, I'd check where that pathetic prick Chapman had gunned down John; thinking about the complicated, psychotic minds of attention seekers like him. There was nothing complicated in Rosa's dark brown eyes. Her chocolate smooth skin and luscious lips soothed and smothered any Hoisting tension built up earlier in the day. Younger than me, an illegal immigrant in more ways than one, she gunned me down with ease the moment I looked into those huge Galaxy Minstrels. I'd bring her gifts Hoisted from stores like Bloomingdales – carrier bag an' all. She'd caress, pamper and put me at ease, treating me like a lost husband returning from a civil war. The Medellin maid knew how to make me feel like a King in his chair.

Rosa being a strict, practicing Catholic – me lapsed – I got the guilt trip when she fluttered those Galaxy Minstrels at me when receiving an expensive stolen gift. But, once she led me to her bed, the guilt took flight somewhere high over Central Park. With me being a minor detail freak, the Dakota building became my New York based St. Paul's the conscience twanger, as I raised a prayer to the spirit of John Lennon that I often pictured walking through the doors whenever I passed.

My Columbian addiction informed me that her and her girlfriends loved beautifully coloured feathered birds. It was apparently a South American girl thing. So, walking the city streets one day I spied a very expensive cockatiel caged inside a huge pet store. Biding my time till the shop was sufficiently busy I trounced in and opened the cage. Without beak attack, the grey, red and yellow bird seemed somewhat drugged. Grabbing it with two hands, I stooped to stuff it inside my inside Hoisting bin. Once I stood upright it must've woken, as it started to flap and struggle. I swiftly made my exit with one side of my coat making ghost movements. Suddenly, Durante, as I named him, started to flutter wildly. I punched the side of my coat twice, as passing New Yorkers stared. I knew the third punch had hit home when he stopped flapping and struggling. I'd knocked Durante out.

Opening the trunk of Seamus' car, parked on a lot nearby, I reached in and took the re-awakened, squawking bird and lashed him inside. Later that day, I returned to the Pet Store and walked out with the most expensive cage; the one that was a Parrot's four star penthouse, and returned to Seamus' apartment block. Retrieving Durante from his trunk-jail he looked sad. I felt sad. After a brief struggle I put him inside his new home and he perked-up immensely, as I fed him some pieces of apple and peanut butter sandwich. My new Columbian cutie treated me like the King of King's when I presented her with her new companion, Durante, the happy cockatiel.

Walking New York with Rosa, my coffee coloured Belinda Carlisle, I noticed heads turning as fellers, and ladies, second glanced. Chomping on Baby Ruth's while running my other hand across her gorgeous backside, for the briefest, I felt tall as the Empire State. Sadly, I ended in a state, when she told me she couldn't see me for a while as her Yankee soldier boyfriend was back in town and soon she'd marry him. Her family had slaved and saved to send 'the good looking one', as she put it – and I couldn't argue – to the United States, with a sole purpose and promise to return with a Tom Cruise husband, a prized Green Card, and money for her younger siblings to make the same trip north to Dollar Central.

I admired her independence and arrow like ambition and met her at the Dakota Building again, once GI Joe had rifled on out. But, being gung-ho in our own personal strivings was always going to cause friction, then conflict. Not wanting to spoil a beautiful relationship, I graciously, but achingly let her fade from view. All beautiful things must pass...Like a high earning shop though, Rosa was hard habit to break.

Catching a flight to Liverpool, via London, family questioned my gallivanting ways, tanned looks and drip dry outfits. With increasingly good cash flow, London mortgage man got me finance on a posh Liverpool apartment, which the brother eventually moved into. I halved the mortgage payments with him, while allowing my mother a personal £200 allowance that I sent home each month. Apparently the local housing market was on the up. Duly checking that sod all else was, I jumped the Rattler back to London to make a fresh claim on my lapsed handout. McRent being paid directly by the

Social was not what I wanted. Spanner, for a small fee, now had a paying job as he signed for all three of us. The Tories didn't care so neither did we.

10

WISH YOU WERE HERE

After visiting Boney and Paddy – due out – and some Hoisting along the High Streets of London, I wanted back in doughnut country. The Yanks go on about everything being bigger, and, including hat size and waistbands, they usually are, and though there's probably more history and culture in a Laura Ashley tweed jacket, everything being open and spacious suited my persistent need to ramble. Paddy had asked about my 'Wish you were here' postcards sent from the U.S. Eastern seaboard. Him being pinned down, I didn't have the gall to tell him how great everything was.

A blink of a weekend in Majorca, on a Lladdro ramble, and Lenny and me had to bubble-wrap fifteen expensive statues lifted from the many porcelain shops in Palma, C'an Picafort and Porto Pollensa, along with other smaller holiday resorts dotted around the island. Though a couple were broken in-transit they were expertly super glued and sold in days. The statue graft was a great earner as Vinny sold the figurines with ease to high class London buyers. Brumble took half of them.

No sooner had we touched down than a whistle-stop journey around the main cities of Norway, Sweden and Denmark saw us return with expensive winter leathers and furs. Brumble had skiing acquaintances who'd often ask if there was any Scandinavian skiing equipment for sale. Vinny said Brumble loved supplying his Yuppified mates with only the best goods. It felt great sending only the most expensive skiing equipment home in boxed parcels, knowing you'd be touching down at Heathrow to a welcome with wages.

Lenny, struggling to keep pace, had me seated on a transatlantic flight from London alone. Arriving at Newark Airport, Seamus rammed golf course leaflets, Hotel flyers and maps of the Eastern States in my face on touchdown. Seamus of the hungry eyes; hungry for earners, hungry for learners with a gargantuan appetite for life, *in person*, was like an airport exit bag of speed! If you'd recently been through divorce, bereavement or illness, this fella, you needed to see. Back in America with the Electric Bono and me back in town, we were once again ready to ramble.

Hitting the outskirts of Philadelphia and Washington, it was strange when Seamus took me on a visit to the White House and parked the car nearby with a boot full of golf apparel, bags and clubs. Style, mpg and comfort didn't matter with hire cars, as long as it had a boot like an obese Dracula coffin and could cover the ground like the gangster car from the Wacky Races. Crossing City traffic, I was wary of transport violation that could lead to a pull, but Seamus was such a fine Hoisting Jockey I could sightsee in utter comfort with good earnings in place. And, unlike in England, where Plod would check you and your accent out, Seamus had such a good professional Caddy story lined up that the busy Yank Bizzies wouldn't get further than a traffic ticket.

Mileage never fazed him, and with U2 and a host of Wolftones rebel songs never off the car stereo I was soon getting a daily lesson in Irish rebel history in verse. Emmett, Barry, Connolly, McDermott, McBride, I knew all the names, and after one long highway journey from New York to Boston their names were slam-dunked into my memory box for good. After one Cork or Dublin uprising song too many I asked him to stick my Pink Floyd tapes on, which he did, but he said made you miserable. Playing him Floyd's *The Wall* album, with its white brick cover and concept theme, he told me it was 'a bit different' but switching to 'Dark Side of the Moon' he reckoned that after half an hour of *that* I might as well drive the hire car straight over him as it sounded like British suicide music. Different musical tastes completely.

He got his own way musically, as even when I'd offer driving respite it would never be for more than an hour. Those long American highway drives became my Irish history lessons. Arriving back in New York thirsty and tired he often took me to a couple of those New York Noraid boozers, but after reluctantly dropping a dollar in the collection box I concluded that the customers and staff were delusional and most of these Yankee IRA sympathisers would run a mile before going to war for 'the cause'. Romantic notions from afar, I told them all on numerous occasions that they didn't know how lucky they were that their kin had once set sail for kinder shores. Taking a place for granted I think they call it.

Car hire being cheap, we drove the tastiest motors with the biggest boot space: Dodge's, Buick's and fat-arsed Ford's, massive gas guzzlers, resembling living rooms on wheels. Being used to dinky English Ford's and rusty Vauxhalls, American cars looked liveable and ready to move into, to me. We started stacking leftover boot space with cartons of cigarettes, as some Southern States had different tax laws and were much cheaper than New York. They helped stop the clubs, shoes and golf carts rattling around the cavernous trunk, but once they were paid for and loaded I became much more security conscious about the car.

Normally, with not paying for anything, I'd be lax when it came to locking the boot and doors (we always had two sets of keys), and sometimes I'd leave the keys hidden under a tyre or seat in case I got collared and cuffed and my captors, after searching me, would want to know where the getaway vehicle lay. Once switch-off arrived and your brain had been highly tuned to overload for the last three hours, I'd become so laidback that I'd say to Seamus, 'You locked the doors?' If he replied no, I'd tell him it was unimportant as we hadn't paid for the stuff anyway. But once the cigarettes were paid for and we'd spent money I'd be double-checking all the time. It was my English, street-crime head over thinking. Seamus told me not to worry. In the States, car crime, the wrecking of phone boxes and other petty thievery was not as prevalent as inner-city Britain, but a Cranky Yankee stateside mugger wouldn't think twice about blowing you away for fifty bucks. Like tastes in humour and chocolate it was a different mindset, somewhat akin to drunken English 'fighting down a jigger' compared to screw loose American's 'quick to pull the trigger'.

Seamus said we had to watch for mobsters not cops when it came to tobacco runs. Apparently there were turf wars over where you did business in New York, and selling cheap cigarettes in certain areas was controlled by Italian, Hispanic, Irish and Black gangs that wouldn't take kindly to new kids arriving on Quick-buck block. It was a sideline I left to Seamus, who seemed happy that I didn't interfere or ask questions about profit. If he made more than me, or more than he let on, I didn't care. Swag-wise, like Vinny, he kept stumping up the readies I'd ask for – the usual third of the price tag.

With flights cheap as British rail travel – when you caught the offers – we hopped aboard an American Airlines flight to Savanna, Georgia, before taking a hire car drive over to Hilton Head on the South Carolina coast. Seamus reckoned it was a fishing and golfing holiday hot-spot not to be missed. When I asked did he mean tranquil and scenic, he replied that he meant it was A1 Hoisting country (he now used the word). Vinny would've laughed at his pronunciation. I did each time he uttered it.

Bang on with his assessment, it was such a lovely place we stayed for ten days, only upping sticks when a half-force hurricane almost blew us out of town. With eyes firmly glued to mall maps, golf course directions and descriptions, totally ignoring the TV and its weather channels, we nearly came unstuck while out in the wilds of Georgia searching for the next course to hit. Good thing about the heavy drizzle was that an English-type raincoat didn't look out of place, and golf apparel and clubs found their way to inside pockets at an alarming rate...

Talking alarms, one on-course golf shop had boarded its windows in case the half-hurricane (no such thing I know) became a full force bungalow-banger, and we ended up setting the alarm off after climbing in with the place deserted. Parking the Dodge we ran to the safety of the clubhouse dodging branches, sand and various bits of golf course that flew about our ears. The courses around Hilton Head SC and Eastern Georgia were left so undermanned that we had to send three parcels of swag over ground to New York and two parcels overseas to Vinny and Left Foot in London. Like most of the States, Hilton Head Island was a place you could breathe. I've revisited the place for breathing holidays on several occasions.

Back at New York HQ, Seamus told me he had another Hispanic beauty lined up to meet me Saturday night. A Jennifer Lopez lookalike, Barmaid, she had apparently suggested she liked 'English gentlemen' with a few bucks to burn. I'd learned to avoid the truth; though, I must say, I was partly on my way with the second suggestion. Once she bumped into my accent she insisted I was Irish like the rest of the beer and butt-mad barfly's, and only after one thing. Clocking another fantastic Hispanic derriere (better than the Lopez one) I could only agree.

Maria Gonzales of the stereotypical name, and arse, became my on/off New York girlfriend for the next two years. She blew hot and Hispanic at first, but went cold, cynical and critical when she sussed that, through me, she might be able to dress and eat well but she was never going to get the fervently lusted after green card. How I wished they were

Hoistable and not wrapped up in red tape behind the door of some snidey government office. Green cards were like gold to some South Americans, and you could actually win one if your number came up in the unfair, murky migrant lottery.

Within weeks of meeting Maria she was selling perfume and cigarettes as a sideline. Her English wasn't very good but it doesn't take long to learn 'under the counter' 'Chanel' and 'Marlboro's' in broken American-English speak does it? Thing is, she started bringing all these illegal immigrants into a boozer that was IRA friendly and the last thing Frankie the owner wanted was immigration cops sniffing around his premises. Seamus and I had to placate him while telling Maria that we were not being racist, but her South American comrades had to piss off pronto. They had been coming in to buy the odd pack of cigarettes or bottle of perfume, but only able to work a couple of dogsbody hours in slave jobs, or not at all, they were all keen as hot dog mustard for a dime-saving bargain and even keener to sell the swag.

Maria lived in a small apartment with two other girls up in Morningside Heights, not far from Morningside Park. I'd Stroll the length of most of the mid to upper Westside district, all the way up Central Park West to where she lived. Cutting away from Central Park, on any Westside Street, hundred or up, I'd walk by Columbia University and bunk into Riverside Church to get to the top of the beautiful gothic church spire.

The view across the Hudson River, allied to some of the gorgeous tweedy students, would take my breath away, reminding me in some strange way of the River Mersey and its beautiful Mary Ellen's. By the time I reached Maria's place off Eighth Avenue, I was so energised after my early morning New York stroll that I'd be trying to nail her there and then in the lobby. The moment she opened the front door I became Gnasher at the Postman in reverse; me the ravaging Postman and her, the sexy Hispanic bitch – terrible phrase, I know. Dog on heat…I think they call it?

Telling her those curves of hers needed more vertical exercise to tie in with the plentiful horizontal walking she was already doing, she'd moan about wanting to jump the Subway back to the Midtown district from a nearby stop, but I'd agree to ride only after I'd walked a mile or two on the other side of Central Park down Fifth Avenue. Busy doing my touristy thing, Alan Whicker the clothes-nicker loved nothing more than a travelling man, street stroll. Don't know what it is in the air in New York, but if drug dealers could nail it, mail it, rail it then sail it, dirty street-sleet cocaine and talc-tampered speed would soon be redundant drugs of the past.

Put simply, sucking the place in gave me a lasting high that no manufactured poisoned powder could ever match. Maybe, like drugs lose their initial kick for practising drug addicts, New York City eventually does the same for its long term inhabitants? I was never one of those so, forever giving me that platform sole feeling, it never lost its appeal for me. Another plus from getting a daily high from breathing in New York air was that there was no paranoid after downer, like the one after I'd copped the art shop money in London and thought the door and wall's were wafer thin! Paranoid leaving a shop maybe, but New York was a jungle I loved and could easily get lost in. And, nobody knew you! Concerning the city's oxygen, like the song goes: *If they can make it there, surely, they can make it anywhere?* Don't think so!

Edging into Harlem, I'd heard all the stories about how mad, bad and African-rad it was, and I must admit I was a little edgy once I'd edged across the Park and into its streets but walking by Marcus Garvey Park and down past the Shabazz Mosque, where Malcolm X used to minister the way of the Muslim I didn't feel threatened or wary at all. I'd walked Brixton, Toxteth and Moss Side Streets in the UK, and, to me, those places after dark were far more unnerving than New York's Harlem. Maria reckoned I was choosing the nicer streets.

Telling Seamus it was time-off for playtime, Maria and I would go downtown and board the Staten Island ferry to visit Ellis Island and the recently restored Statue of Liberty, before having lunch in any of a zillion lower Manhattan delis. Mid-afternoon, we'd venture back uptown and visit the Bronx Zoo, the Rockefeller Centre, or some rocket-lidded skyscraper like the Chrysler or Empire State building; or, wander the Metropolitan museum of Art, prior to heading home. Maria loved art, museums and the theatre and I indulged in a little cultural tourism, but the call of Saks, Bloomingdale's and Broadways bright lights and shops had me impatient to leave before the true essence of why we'd first entered had ever sunk in. I did get to see Charles Dickens *'The Life and Adventures of Nicholas Nickleby'* at The Broadhurst theatre...I think, and Douglas Furber's *Me and My Girl* at The Marquis on 45th and 46th, but she wanted Joe Orton's *Loot* – about an armed robbery where the money gets stashed in a coffin – which had recently finished and it just wasn't for me.

Her two housemates where squeaky, geeky clean in a strange sexy way: big glasses, big backsides and big, juicy, kissable lips. Squeaky meant Hispanic Catholic cleanliness, padlocked belly warmers and un-waxed moustaches with no chance of any fleshly shenanigans for me. Both were students with medical profession dreams, driven by thoughts of a passport stamped with citizenship, a purse filled with dollars and a future sky emblazoned with a smiling Doctor hubby and the whole starry-eyed American dream.

Same time, Light Fingered Larry dreamed only of getting the three of them into the flock at the same time, then the afterglow, then the added dream of the great designer shop in the sky, where staff couldn't see you Hoisting because you were invisible, and garments of clothing were designed by the Lord himself and cost ten grand upwards for a pair of jeans. Mad, mad logic, mad, mad dreams; again, they say everything is bigger in the States, so I suppose I dreamt bigger. Besides, I must have been high as the World Trade Centre on New York air, when you think the Lord wore a Toga and designer Toga's were always bad sellers like those fat-twat Barry White and Pavarotti pants!

After leaving the museums dotted around Central Park, weighed down with souvenirs from in-house shops, I dropped bagfuls of trinket junk with Maria's housemates, for the illegal immigrants who no longer hung around the Irish bar where she served and where Seamus and I sold swag. After another week long trip down the Eastern seaboard to Virginia and North Carolina I had to stop for breath. Opening a bank account at a Manhattan branch of the Bank of America, I now had my Big Time Elvis account up and running. Easy-peasy to open pre 9/11, I only had to show passport ID as a foreign national and 4,000 USD in cash and they welcomed me with dollar-eyed open arms. More straightforward than in the UK, anytime you flashed cash in the US, it got you an instant walkover.

Deciding to take the long road back from North Carolina, through parts of Pennsylvania, in case we missed a Golden Nugget golf course, it hit me just how cash-conscious I'd become and how money-mad the Americans really were. Driving by Pittsburgh all you kept hearing about was Andrew Carnegie and how he was once the richest man in the world from all the money he'd made in steel, and about the town of Hershey, where Milton S Hershey had built his wealth relying on people with a sweet tooth, before building a chocolate town named after himself. If Hershey had built an empire from crap chocolate then I'm sure Cadbury's could push on to own the world if they choose.

Fact is: America and Americans are seriously dough orientated, dosh educated and greenback mad! If you've got pocketfuls of dollars, you get doors opened for you at the likes of the Waldorf Astoria. If your brassick with that grey welfare demeanour about you, you'll get kicked to the floor and treated like street lino till you eventually get up and find some. Its cut and dried with hardly a liberal question asked. Put simply: it's kind'a like dough means go! And, crumb's is for bums!

Avoiding chaotic big cities and their traffic jams (unlike Britain most shopping malls were in the suburban outskirts) we went by Philadelphia and its famous liberty bell, finding our way to the smaller and neater Gettysburg near the Maryland border, to witness the Civil War battleground where fifty thousand men had lost their lives. Now that place was interesting, even for couldn't-keep-still Seamus. We even found time to learn about the Eastern State Penitentiary, where Al Capone had spent time and which Charles Dickens had set out to see on his arrival in 1842. Dickens had once remarked that he wanted to view the Gothic prison and Niagara Falls more than anywhere else stateside. On passing through Philly on interstate 95, when not far from the historical jail, I remarked to Seamus that I'd rather eat five bars of Hershey's chocolate than view 'that place'. He agreed.

As the autumn/fall arrived, Maria, getting more familiar, asked if she could go shopping with me. I knew what she meant, and didn't want to start mixing business with pleasure. I'd already given her some tasty underwear, dresses and shoes I'd swapped for golf clubs, with another Irish-American knock-off acquaintance of Seamus's. Getting cheeky, and hinting, she'd shown me the fancy department store, Bergdorf Goodman, and told of the pricey ladies garments that lay inside.

I hardly ever touched women's wear, not unless it fell off a mannequin dummy and into my lap, or, it had been passed to me by another street hustling Hoister. Firstly: women were too fussy. Secondly: you had to get the exact size, colour and fitting for the buyer, because…they were so fussy. And thirdly: they would take all day trying something on, finally buy it, before changing their minds next day, because…they were fussy! Fast-earners did not marry at all well with fussiness, and with a No Returns policy forever in operation, you'd only give a buyer their money back in extenuating circumstances – like if their parents had died and they needed money for funeral arrangements. Women's clothes were more than just awkward to move; they had to be in fashion, needed ironing and even had to smell just right.

Before I returned to Blighty Seamus and I decided to head North to New England. He introduced me to a couple of Moroccan shoplifters whose names I could never pronounce, but who were good competition in the Westside selling rights and, slick operators in their own right. I'd been on a couple of New York walkabouts with the one I called Ali. He was good, but our language barrier and the fact I thought he had suspicious features meant there was never any future in Hoisting together. Not that I wanted it anyway, but, thinking process: *you never know what you might learn?*

Allied to Seamus's golf course and shopping mall research, the two Moroccan lads reckoned New England – the Connecticut, Massachusetts, New Hampshire and Rhode Island part – was a Hoister's paradise, full of rich little towns with rich little pickings. We had to leave promptly, before it got too cold and before the golf courses closed; and, as Seamus directly put it: 'You never, never know, we could be stuck in Sing Sing or the Eastern State Penn this time next year'. If that was his idea of a joke, I hardly laughed. And, anyway, like Seamus' sense of humour, the Eastern State Penn had closed down years ago!

Returning to London, Paddy and Boney had been nicked again while I was in America. I wrote to them both in jail, but the postcards from around the World seemed a little insensitive. Aside from not wanting to brag about my next port of call, they hardly ever wrote back. Once released, Vinny told me Boney had moved to Stoke Newington with a good looking North London girl, who Vinny reckoned was a druggie; otherwise she wouldn't have been hanging on Boney's arm. Paddy had said his goodbyes to Vinny before moving back to

Liverpool to graft with his mad Uncle Tommy. My final letters asking them to cross the Atlantic got blanked. Maybe they thought I'd actually become a Big Time Charlie? Such are the choices in life? Through Liverpool Lullabies and family I heard about them from time to time. That, and a fleeting glimpse apart, I never saw either of them again for years.

Every place I travelled I set a budget. Every trip had to make profit. I set myself a target of no less than three grand per one man trip. Walking out on expensive meals, hotel bills and not paying for gas...sorry, petrol, as a travelling expense, was restricted to 'only when I/we had to'. If we hadn't Hoisted enough swag, then, we had to! Talking about expenses with Seamus, as we drove toward the city of Hartford, Connecticut, he changed subject and started going on about the rock band Toto coming from there and it being the Insurance capital of the States. Ignoring the Hartford history lesson, I told him about North and South politics in the UK and why we had to have an expenses plan worked out so that I could return one day and not have to listen to any old Johnno's. He couldn't believe how passionate I got when mentioning British Tories and their policies. 'See Seamus, it's Ok for you to earn a few dollars then go back to New York to spend it all in the bars round Hell's Kitchen, but it's a bigger plan that drives me!'

Car in cruise control, he studied me for a moment. 'I hear what you're saying, but what has expenses and walking out on hotel bills got to do with British politicians?'

'Well, they're the type of places they stay in, what the British tax payer pays for. If they had their way, they'd have no one with my accent anywhere near the place!'

'But what's that got to do with expenses?'

'They can live off other people's taxes, and lie and steal and cheat the voting population, but I'll stay in the best room and no one will pay!'

'But surely the Hilton Hotel will pay if you walk out of the place?'

'I couldn't give a shit! They're just the American Tories, and as long as the money stays in mine and your bin and not in any Tories back pocket, I'm happy!'

My logic could be somewhat twisted, but he enjoyed it when I told him all about the real Britain that I knew. More importantly, filling up at the next busy petrol station, and driving off without paying, I knew he was bang with the programme. Gas was cheap in the States but, till we earned, it was free! Back in Hell's Kitchen, most of his drinking buddies still thought Britain was full of upper-crust Tory toff's, and some of them annoyed me no end when they referred to me as a dirty Brit, and one of Maggie's boys? Though they thought of themselves as rebels, they were 'Right On' with the good ol' US of A, their country of birth. While I, rootless, detached, holding no allegiance to any flag, and a long, long way from home, I was the only one carrying rebellion on board. I eventually thought of their rebellion, rooted in romanticized Irish history, as laughable! Fucking 'talk is easy' gang of Barfly's!

Within a year of keeping with the expenses plan I had bought another apartment in the New York area. Seamus' Irish Mother, Patsy, from Limerick, had retired out to Brentwood, Long Island, and sold household swag, linen, ornaments and antiques for us whenever we raided Eastern seaboard home stores. She'd been told we were buying them wholesale to make a profit; otherwise, she wouldn't have touched the stuff with any of the array of fancy walking sticks that Seamus and I had procured for her from stuffy New England Antique shops. She was a 'God-botherer' of the highest order, and might as well have slept on a bench inside St Anne's church. Making good money herself, supplying and taking orders from an ageing congregation, Patsy put most of it in the St Anne's collection box, before lighting her daily candle and kneeling to say prayers. Anytime we were due payment, on both knees to the Mother Mary, that's where we found her.

Visiting her one day she told me how Brentwood used to

be called Modern Times, and had been started out in 1850 by two mad anarchist's, but had since been renamed Brentwood after the town in Essex, England. Seamus' Mother Patsy could tell stories like no one I'd met. Telling us about Josiah Warren and Stephen Pearl Andrews, the town's elder statesman, they had apparently made a ruling of individual sovereignty, and had started the colony with no ruling authority, courts, Jails or Police, using labour exchange and a bartering system as currency. The fact its origins flew in the face of Imperialism and the way of the British ruling classes and Royal Family was what had made her originally stop there. It intrigued me too.

She made the place sound so interesting that I bought an apartment in the same block as her, near St Anne's RC Church where she really lived. Up for sale in a repossession auction, her good name put me front of the queue. Surprisingly, the non-status mortgage was easier to get at the Bank of New York than in Barclay's or any other Building Society or Bank in Britain?

Lifted only twice in the next ten years, Seamus used the apartment as a bolt hole whenever it wasn't rented out; though he preferred staying downtown in Hell's Kitchen being a homeboy New Yorker. The place only got sold when his lovely Mother eventually passed away. I was all over the place and loving life. The next ten years were an inter-mingled, continent switching, Hoisting collage that these on-pier skaters will never give me enough switch off time to tell you about. Maybe someday, when a category five hurricane smashes the pier to bits!

SEE EMILY PLAY

Mid 90's British Airway's Plane to Japan

Japan, Hong Kong and the general Asian area on the World map had become my new Hoisting ground to conquer. Not tiring of travelling the globe, I'd found Japan and its culture shock nothing short of exhilarating! The luxury hotels had deep baths that were shorter in length; the people in service wore white gloves in case they passed germs; they individually wrapped grapes and plums and, they looked and dressed differently. The trains ran with such efficiency that I laughed every time I boarded, when thinking about hiding in the bogs on a Euston bound British Rail rattler! With everything around the Japanese archipelago being expensive, same as Switzerland and Scandinavia, my old habit of bunking trains and out of hotels meant every trip remained profitable.

With an on/off Hispanic girlfriend in New York, an English Rose career woman in London, and family all ensconced in Liverpool, I was getting a little weary of being a man with no real nest to return to. I had bolt holes, places to stay at and magnificent hotels galore, but grandeur and material things had never tickled me. I just liked the freedom in having money, and not having to jump when some Tory Bread-head or Lord or Lady Haw Haw felt like telling me to. I'd seen my Father graft to feather Lord Haw Haw's mansion nest, and my Father's Father build then go to war to keep his fortified mansion wall's intact. No, those days were long gone! My family had benefitted, my companions had benefitted but, and sort of suddenly, I knew I wanted children. New York girl and London lady both wanted career commitment that I couldn't give. I tried reasoning my point, but it always reached the point where I'd be telling them I'd like children that they wouldn't give!

Having recently visited the main islands of Hokkaido, Honshu, Shikoku and Kyushu, I was now sat on a British Airways schedule flight making my way back to the customer friendly department stores of Tokyo when a beautiful lady approached. I'd spoken with her before on my last flight to Japan. Always good to hear the native dialect from my own city of birth, Emily had told me she was from Waterloo, North Liverpool and that she'd been an Air Hostess for British Airways for two years.

'Excuse me, Mickey isn't it.'

'Hello Emily, I see they're looking after you then.'

She looked around the cabin somewhat confused. I got to the point. 'The new uniform, it looks brilliant on you!'

She blushed a little. 'Oh thanks. So, where you off to now?'

'Tokyo then Kobe; just business to attend to.'

'I'd avoid Kobe if I was you. Since the earthquake the place is wrecked!'

Over five thousand people had been killed in a massive earthquake recently. Me, wearing my Westerner goggles every waking day had quickly forgotten about the tragedy and, I hadn't been near the great port of Kobe since 1993. Emily was charming, Liverpool funny, interested in the world, but more than anything she was gorgeous! Cheekily I asked to meet her at her Hotel in Tokyo the following day. After having a fried noodle meal, instead of the hated Sushi or cold meat dishes, we spent the day sightseeing. From that day forward New York girl and London lady didn't matter.

I stopped seeing both of them immediately. My previous lack of solid commitment meant neither was truly heartbroken. Though, my Argentinean beauty, Camila, decided to relieve my back pocket of $300, which she denied. I'd mistakenly taken Camila on a reconnaissance, mooching mission to her home country, but found places like Buenos Aires were not worth the air fare. Hoisting in Argentina and Brazil, and South America for that matter, were like going Shoplifting in the Aldi! Leaving her rented apartment in the Mott Haven part of The Bronx, for good, I called her the sister of Diego, and told her she belonged in the nearby Rikers Island Prison. She laughed me out the door, telling me that if I hung around any longer it'd be me going to Rikers as soon as she called the Cops! Jumping a cab to Seamus' favourite bar, I had to smirk when I thought of that cheating cow and how I'd furnished her flat from top to bottom!

Flying back to Liverpool via Heathrow, I met Emily at Liverpool's Albert Dock. She instantly made the city a brighter place. It felt great to be home. I took a taxi ride down the Dock Road to the old steel warehouse. Expecting it to be condemned or demolished, there it stood in all its Masonic glory. Emily, sarcastically calling me a true romantic, waited inside the cab while I entered its doors. Staff looked at me curiously. It had new owners. I don't know why I made the trip but, there you go? Emily was infectious. I stayed with her for a few days at the Adelphi Hotel, but didn't want to leave. Meeting whenever we could, over the coming months I took her to Brazil and Peru, and eventually proposed to her on the beach in Rio de Janeiro.

Within a year we'd married in Vegas, honeymooned in Florida – taking the Disney Cruise liner for a five day stint in Nassau – and bought our first house in the posh North Liverpool suburb of Formby. From the moment I spilled the beans about what I did for a living, and Emily didn't bite my head off or walk away, I knew I had to change lifestyles.

Pregnant from our honeymoon, I knew my Hoisting around the planet had to stop. It almost did for a year, till the light fingered tendencies of Larry again crept into play. Selling my three Big Time Charlie apartments, which were the greatest investments I ever made, we moved into our own detached mansion. I felt like Lord Haw Haw, especially when my ageing Father jokingly called me by that name.

For five or six years life was as good as it was ever going to get. We had a baby boy, a brother for our beautiful daughter. My business was running alongside some serial Hoisting that went mainly unnoticed. But, once business associates became customers, and I realized just how much I had to lose, everything started to get a little fucked-up fuzzy! The Capitalist machine seemed to have me in a vice like grip, and that, had never really been my plan. Walking the dog around Formby beach I hatched a new plan that would let me and my family escape forever.

12

WELCOME MY SON, WELCOME TO THE MACHINE

Ensconced in the smothering respect-ability of English suburbia: a wife, two kids, a window replacement company and a detached house in Curtain Peep County, I was a Klepto wearing an upper-middle class mask. Domesticity, material possessions and the wheels of industry I found completely boring. Family meant everything, but sometimes restlessness could be a right pain in the pink rosette. Dragging them outdoors on walkabouts every opportunity, we took more holidays and weekend breaks than Judith Chalmers. Watching evening TV, itchy feet dangled from my legs not Christmas slippers. Old habits, attempting to die hard, lurked just below the cushions of each new leather suite we bought. The kids went to the finest school, we grocery shopped at Marks and Sparks and Sainsbury's, lived in one of the nicest home's in the trendiest area, but, out shopping, manners and practices remained those of a street urchin scallywag.

I never mixed with anybody from the past, drank in town or kept up with Liverpool lullabies (hometown gossip). Finding newspaper's full of miserable, gory glory stories, I'd only buy one if a major headline like 9/11, Diana dying or Elizabeth Taylor or Rod Stewart staying married beyond their honeymoon's got reported. Living alongside Headmasters, Solicitors and Police Chiefs – bubble-wrapped in cashmere comfort – I only felt the goose pimples of being fully alive when I pretended or acted like I was still hungry. Detached mansion meant detached from the past, as I'd completed a lot of mileage since being a crowbar kid from a concrete-grey council estate in Huyton, Liverpool.

The sale of three properties had made me a small fortune, but having wedge had become boring. Sounds stupid, I know, but how else do you explain goods – when needed or simply wanted – continually waltzing out the door. Never stingy, the competition of me against shop technology, security and staff had become my addiction. Items too big to be hidden on person meant bank holiday Monday crowds, the anonymity of wearing a suit, and being older and looking the part, all helped towards me to walking out of electrical and DIY Superstores with the finest goods on offer. Like all jobs, the apprenticeship followed by years practising the practical, meant Hoisting had become second nature.

Hotpoint washing machines, Flymo lawn mowers, Stag furniture, it was all do-able, especially mad Mondays, with bigger the store normally equating to bigger the item. A lot of feller's hate paying a tenner for shaving blades, but if in Boots or Superdrug you took the whole display you were Gillette G2'd for the next three years. Lawn mower getting rusty: try B&Q for a wheel-out bank holiday Monday. Toaster jammed with breadcrumbs: pick up a piece of tasty luggage any busy Saturday afternoon at Debenhams, before venturing over to the electrical department to place the snazziest art deco toaster inside, prior to departure.

It seemed materially I'd cracked it and didn't know where to materialize next. Thinking a legit company would present new goals, it did...for six months. Once I got the window company up and running, I started running away from its panes and panels soon as possible. Trusting people I'd put in charge, and paying them well, I ended up leaving boring window business to them. It was tedious, it didn't change.

Worse, most of the people seemed to be glassy-eyed, sleep-walkers in suits!

People within my small circle had me as a wheeler dealer: a man who got goods at a price. And yeah, to a man, Coppers, Club Captains, Doctors and Teachers, they were all up for a bargain – no questions asked! What they didn't know – brothers and missus apart – I was the one pilfering most of the stuff they ordered. Keeping up appearances, part of my persona was I got hold of things for less than retail, like a middle man or, in street terms: a fence. In reality, I was the risk-taking, bottom man on the shoplifting frontline, while also being the flush-mush, top man who took all the sausage and mash. Strange thing, I still believed in God and went to church. Religion wasn't evil to me, just 'mans' willingness in going to war to impose his religion on everybody else was evil. Through a couple of outer body thingies, and other coincidental stuff, I knew in my mind there was a Creator – a God…I know, and, my opinion by the way.

Knowing what I did was wrong had me stop-starting, making futile attempts to pack it in for good. In my righteous manner, I deemed when younger, marginalised by a heartless Tory government and flat broke…sorry, skint, maybe there was an excuse for my behaviour, but now I'd climbed beyond the bottom rungs this was an addiction of sorts. I had to admit, in one aspect comforting myself, I was a Klepto! Giving it a label helped, like it was my own vice and, didn't everybody have one or two of those. And, according to Hoisters logic mine wasn't that bad. I'd nurtured an itchy-fingered part of me that was going to need a road drill and dynamite to dislodge.

Sometimes, with son and daughter alongside, I'd slip expensive goods up a sleeve or into a coat. Safe from younger eyes, they became aware as they grew that Daddio often liked to walk up shopping aisles alone, and sometimes he'd give them gifts after not stopping at the till point. Business ideas, hoping to get un-hooked, came and went. Taking the entrepreneurial path into market stalls, a hairdresser's, a carwash, a newsagents, vending machines, window frames, and other smaller enterprises, did nothing to cure a raging habit! Only the window company showed any signs of going the course, and that was due to letting others run it.

Helping conscience, I aided charities. Donor to the local church, I dropped monthly bags of clothing, toys and electrical goods that got sent to war ravaged countries like Bosnia, and persistently starving African states that Geldof and the pop stars had tried to feed. The priest blessed me for my kind offerings. Unable to look him in the eye, I bowed in confused shame. Living outside the 'norm', I climbed dough mountain hoping salvation would hit me in the form of a business enterprise I truly loved. As years flew and realization hit that, being a Klepto was more fun, more interesting and a job you could do alone (away from the torridly boring and somewhat more bent wheels of industry – albeit with the social stigma attached) I settled under its banner and tried accepting my itchy-fingered way.

Arrested no more than six times, jailed only once, I suppose my pain in punishment never exceeded my need to change. Prisoners will tell you all about jail: what it did to their soul, how it changed them, while a lot of ex-cons blame it for hard times and the learning of mischievous ways? To me, it was nothing more than a degrading Zero Star Hotel where you went for a good, long sleep. Apart from adding to my aversion to human brown smoke, I don't think it shaped or changed my character one little bit!

Bluntly: the Zero Star Hotel was akin to being unable to leave the door of a McRents Chicken Coop. If they'd thrown me into a Victorian hell hole where hard labour was fuelled with cockroach butties, a swampy mattress and shit-stained nakedness, maybe I'd think differently. But, unwise Liberalisation meant, they didn't and, I don't. It's why I don't over elaborate on the gaff. Basic living levels apart, jail was like the wheels of industry and business: it confined, bored and stifled creativity – all at the same time! Add living in middle class suburbia to the yawn list too; well, at least till something seriously rattled the drapes behind your double-glazed windows.

Though church, religion and spiritual belief brought brief solace, they also brought guilt and dread that the karma of bad be-gets bad would someday dismantle my cashmere comfort and leave my family, like me in Dock Road days, snatching for crumbs down Welfare Walk. Family brings love but, family brings fear; an emotion I'd hardly known my whole life, especially after seeing the white light. Once children become a part of you then, I suppose, same as shoplifting brought you material goods and money, children brought you love and fear – fear of a penniless future I'd once been attuned to, fear of social stigma if friends and neighbours found out about Daddies itchy fingers, and fear of losing a Father and respect to jail and no self-esteem. Understanding this, I dismissed the emotion with a steel shutter that came down fast as a Nat West counter screen during a violent bank robbery!

Knowing drastic action – not some new hobby or business scheme – would be the only chance I had of stopping, was not a thought conducive to happiness or health. From health, wealth and happiness, I had two and a half, so, being a striver and conniver I had to have all three. Unattainable over the course of a lifetime, I know, but, striving personality meant I still had to battle for the full set. Toddling along on a respectable two and a half, striving and conniving took a bolt to the neck one night in Curtain Peep, when the drapes behind our double glazing finally got rattled from dust-laden familiarity by an in-coming ill wind. Being unprepared jolted me and the curtains back to Dock Road days and a sense of fear for family I'd never really grasped before.

A spate of burglaries had left the people of Formby a little late night, noise wary; me, mine and the curtains included. A crew had been breaking into the houses of the so-called well-to-do, stealing anything of note: jewellery, cash, laptops etc, before taking the keys to expensive vehicles parked on driveways. It seemed the homes targeted often held the snazziest wheels on the block paving. 'The fishing technique', where thieves poked a stick through a door knocker or pet-flap to hook keys on offer, was used. 'Crook-hook' it's often called. Criminals often think they know all the tricks, and that they are wise and un-robbable. Victim-wise, due to know-all nonchalance, they're often the easiest sweet for another robber to choose from the Quality Street tin!

Gearing for the new millennium, I started a night and day school course in building surveying, hoping to start the year 2000 on a level and more righteous slab of rock. At first the ins and outs of construction seemed interesting and duly gave thought process some structure. But, ten weeks in, it began to sound as interesting as the rock' n' roll lifestyle of a house brick. Being a quick learner, I read the thousand-page Bob the builder book on slab to roof but, when it came to boggle-eyed math's, grades of sand, and clout nail or Philips screw, my interest slid downhill faster than Franz Klammer with the runs!

Soon the college held customers, not students and teachers. Talking with classmates at tea break, astounded how long some had been on this and other courses, I wondered just how they got by? Some held degrees and had qualified at other respectable professions. I'm thinking: *some of these never want to leave school;* as though they wanted to remain jammed-up with theory, academic practice and school corridors, in order to avoid the concrete paving stones of practical reality! Surveying studies weren't hard, they were boring. So, I suppose they were hard. After maintaining a lifetime interest in construction that, fast diminished once the basic nuts and bolts were explained, I was once again a Klepto?

Near the South Mersey sea front, the college at Riversdale was a decent drive cross town from my North Liverpool,

Formby home. Parked inside the college grounds, I noticed my new motor dazzled among the Student's and Teacher's Riversdale rusties. Like me, it didn't fit. Soon as settled among classmates and class, selling Halfords car parts, along with my usual wares, became part of the reason I turned up – the main part!

Heading home one night, I pulled into a retail park to lift some ordered motor accessories before getting home for tea. A Building Teacher/Surveyor I'd gotten friendly with said his wife's Volkswagen Golf needed an alarm, a stereo and few bits and bobs that could get me a quick hundred quid and, no matter how I invested or wealthy I got, a quick hundred quid was what I was about. The same Teacher introduced me to a land/house building deal, which looked Premier league, legit earning, something that towered above and beyond my Klepto ways. It also looked a surefire investment for my family's future...

After buying an expensive piece of dirt we'd oversee the building of five detached executive homes. Trusting him, and it, I sank most of my savings into the venture as a money laundering, get-rich-slow exercise. Back in-store, with recent home burglaries a secondary thought, blimping a heavy steel wrench, it departed with the pre-ordered bits. Security tags, everywhere by now, meant rooting through individual part boxes for sticky bugs was a right pain in the backside. Lying in bed that night, I tried explaining a little house brick rock' n' roll to my missus from my Bob the Builder book. Like me, she fell asleep with excitement!

The peaceful place we lived – too quiet at times – suited a light sleeper. In the wee wee hours my eyes opened to blackness when I thought I heard sounds from downstairs. Like scurrying mice, the noise continued. Not wanting to wake the kids or my wife, I sat up, listening intently. Blaming shop-lifting dreams, the noise abated. Thinking it must be whistling draught, scattering winter debris or wild imagination I went to go back to sleep. Creaking stairs cranked me up again. Covers off, totally nude, I felt shivers run through me and over me. I wondered if they came from coldness or being fearful.

Edging to the window, peeping behind the curtain, an unfamiliar car spluttered near the entrance to the Close. The silhouette of a man sat smoking inside. Thinking about calling out to the kids, to see if they were out of bed, I stopped. If someone was in the house it would only scare the children, while letting intruders know I was awake and aware. The creaking grew increasingly louder. Frozen on the spot, I knew I felt the presence of another person. Reaching slowly behind the bedside cupboard, I felt for the wrench.

It seemed fated that the day I pick up a weapon of self-defence could be the first day to use it. I thanked the Lord I had. Unfrozen by being armed, tip toeing to the bedroom door, I tried spying around the small opening. Wanting to open it more, I hesitated. I knew the door creaked. Pressing an eye against a cold steel hinge, I figured a male frame in the darkness and shivered again, uncontrollably. The person edged toward the centre of the landing and stopped. Thinking they'd seen me, I moved from the opening. Not breathing at all, seconds lapsed...

Controlling flow, I breathed gently in and out. The door creaked slowly open. A head appeared, then a bending frame. Taking aim, I baseball batted the man full-whack on the temple. The dull thud meant solid connection. Aware of nothing else around me, I waited as he half-collapsed to the floor before striking him again, and again! The thud of steel wrench impacting on skull journeyed up my arm, registering in my brain. Moaning, he crawled toward the stairs. Hunched over him, I let him move. Immediately above the stairwell, I kicked him hard with bare feet. The impact felt weak compared to the wrench. Taking aim for his reflected bald head, I struck him so hard I thought I might've killed him. He bounced off the wall and every stair on his way down.

Badly wanting him out, I followed, hovering, edging for more damage. Halfway down, I spied an accomplice entering the doorway. He shouted to leave off. Hesitating, I awoke to the bigger picture. The man on the floor, in a bad way with blood covering most of his face and fleshy head, moaned loudly. I shouted back, 'Get the cunt out of the fucken' house!' Lifting his partner in crime, my wife and kids appeared at the top of the stairs. Doorway man attempted to drag his co-burglar from the porch, as street light danced upon them both. Lamplight glistened from a blood splattered crown. I zoomed in for a better picture and description...

Glimpsing half-open eyes on a tortured face, they seemed familiar. Threateningly, I edged two steps closer, then fully down the staircase. My wife called me back. I angrily hushed her. The scared voice of my youngest child brought me upon my toes like an edging predator. Doorway turned the bald guy around on his back, before cradling him like a baby. There was blood everywhere. Again, I thought I recognized the eyes and face? Yards away, I moved closer. A dithering hand came up to wipe at pouring blood. Fleetingly, I caught both eyes. Face recognition clicked like a light switch! Shocked, I swallowed hard. It couldn't be? It was. It was Paddy, Paddy McArdle! Gobsmacked, I let Doorway carry him to the waiting car.

To the corner of my eye the driver jumped out. In a far-off voice he issued threats. Puffing my chest out, I walked toward them. Driver backed off, helping carry and drag baldy to the car. My eldest child's voice pierced my thoughts as she called me. Creeping slowly backward, I stood inside the porch letting them move away. Giving distance, they issued more threats, while bundling him into the car. Again, their voices seemed far-off. Unable to make out what they were saying, the car started and backed up toward the gate. The driver shouted they'd be back. Hearing clearly, I shouted I'd love them to and that they'd die if they did. Foolishly, I threw the wrench at his open window. It sailed over the bonnet. Thinking about running around the motor to fetch it, they sped from the close. Still naked, finding the wrench, I walked the same path as the Vauxhall Astra. It blew exhaust fumes into the crisp air and off into the distance.

While checking the garden, neighbours lights came on. Walking back inside, I closed the door. My wife went to dial the Police. Putting a hand on top of hers, I told her no. About to lock the key, stupidly left in the keyhole each night to stop draught blowing through, it was gone! Opening the door, it wasn't in the keyhole outside. Running upstairs, I put tracksuit bottoms on before searching the path and garden area. The keys had disappeared…so had my chances of relaxing for the coming days!

My missus again told me to phone the Police. I told her it was a waste of time, they'd be long gone by now and forensics would be all over the house for prints and blood. I'd maybe give them a no-names description in the morning? Not wanting Bizzies crawling all over the house was a different type of paranoia. Holding a politically inclined disregard wasn't like a hardened prison con's outlook, who hated the uniform and everything that went with it. Put simply, I didn't want any Plod in my house – end of story!

As weeks flew by, with locks changed, I relaxed well as I could back to cashmere comfort. Not informing family that Paddy had been part of the burglary team was hard to keep up. Meanwhile, I tried to avoid finding out what had happened to him. Though Paddy had a naughty extended family, that, I reasoned, I could handle. Keeping quiet was not wanting to tug at the fabric of my new cashmere existence, or bring attention to, or blow the gaff on my discreet sham of a lifestyle. My mother still knew Paddy's mother, and other people could have gotten me information easily – if I'd asked? But, I'd grown wary of rattling suburban cages or disturbing old dust.

Hoisting inside a local DIY superstore a few months later, I bumped into an old mate, mid-lift, who asked if I'd heard about

Paddy McArdle. While I tried acting normally, he told me he'd been sent to jail as part of a gang who specialized in the robbery of up-market homes in the North of England. A seven year sentence got him diagnosed in prison as having mental problems, due to depression and outbreaks of violence brought on by severe headaches, culminating in a number of attacks on other inmates and prison guards. He'd been sent to a top security mental home with an indefinite release date, and had apparently tried to kill himself on a number of occasions. This fella, my Daily Wail, told me everything I didn't want to hear.

Month later, I got the news Boney had died of a heroin overdose in an Amsterdam hospital. I'd known for years he'd been dabbling with his fucked-up, Cockney sidekick, Danny Felman and a host of other East End low lives, but not to what extent. Boney had been in and out of Southern Slammers for years. In some way, I was glad I'd never seen him before he died.

Days later, hotel room to myself, away on a golfing break at the Belfry with my new respectable *friends,* I pondered how three young lives could have taken such different roads. More importantly, I thought long and hard about if I could've helped in both cases and, was I responsible in any way? Boney and Paddy looked earmarked for a nine-to-five-fodder, labouring life, till I bunked that London train and they met illegality, Felman and iffy graft? Well…it seemed to me?

While the company I kept golfed, I moped. Lying to the group about feeling ill, I hardly left my hotel room for two days. A Police Officer in the group who seemed to take to me more than most, often seeking my company, kept phoning to ask if I felt okay. Fitting, you know, that an Officer of the Law asked the questions that had me telling fibs at this point. The fibs I told him were small fry compared to the fucking big whopper I'd been playing out for almost twenty years!

Phoning my wife, I lied again, saying I was going down to the South coast to see shoe-shop, Lenny Edwards, about some earners. Sneaking from the Belfry golf course, with no good-byes, I headed to Dover Docks and caught the first cross-channel ferry to Belgium. Driving aimlessly, I ended up in Antwerp, scene of many-a-shoe-graft and booked myself into the plushest hotel in town. Wandering about the gothic buildings of the city, especially its churches, for almost a week I tried making sense of how things had panned out.

A couple of weeks later my missus answered a knock at the door to be greeted by two tough looking gents she mistook for Bizzies. Describing them to a tee, I knew their identity straight away. Paddy's extended had come-a-calling. The large burn to one side of the face and neck told me mad Uncle Tommy had started probing. Praying it would go away, I knew in the bulls-eye of my heart it never would. Tommy was a known million-aire drug dealer, the slice'em for the fun of it type, who lived more for the violence, degradation and sleaziness involved in that lifestyle than the mounds of dirty dosh.

Years ago, Paddy had told me all about Tommy's torturous childhood upbringing, to eventual sinister adulthood: the homes, the beatings, the ruthless slaying of rivals; till, like most modern day Gangsters, he ruled the streets he came from while riddling them with shit! Twenty one for life, he'd been taking it out on the world for thirty years now.

Spilling the info to one of my brothers, the house immedi-ately went up for sale with no sign outside. Two weeks after that knock, when Emily had coolly told the callers I'd be back from working in Dubai in a month, we were on a plane to Florida. Taking the kids from school, their teachers were told about my fantastic new job offer in Dubai, as were friends, relations and nosey neighbours who'd noticed the house for sale with a local Estate Agent. Tommy had slowly found out about my part in Paddy's past, but found out fast about my absconding, my land deal/business interest with the Surveyor/Teacher and my family network. Don't ask me how, he just did?

Placing strangleholds on deliveries, construction and building progress, his mob attacked the on-site security, place of work and workers so frequently it eventually went up for sale at a fraction of the price. The Bizzies simply couldn't be bothered with the hassle of Tommy's crew. Thinking about fronting his lackey's or him alone, was a complete no-no. If you shot him or had him shot, you had to do the other six or seven behind him. I'd lost touch with virtually all of my past, while they had a huge army to call on and were still living in it!

With no takers on the horizon, even other powder gangsters won't go anywhere near the piece of land that remains to this day, my ball and chain. Like Boney and Paddy's first jail sentence, and as instant a piece of Karma as you're likely to see, home-invasion...sorry, burglary onwards, everything went tits-up real quick! Finding myself in the comfy place I'd always strived to try and reach, I concluded it wasn't that comfy after all.

In Antwerp, before Tommy had put the wheel clamps on, grasping it was me, and not just the local Jewish diamond contingent who carried that once elusive wad of notes in a back pocket, got me thinking whether all those holidays, life experiences and graft had really made me any-the-wiser? Then, the big one hit! Slowing down to snail's pace, realizing I was the owner of a brain that felt numb, jaded and omelette like, with plenty of strips of ham falling out of the side, it sank into that scrambled head of mine that all the fancy Hotels and Restaurants were now at my disposal, and that I was travelling with a member's pass...

Okay, a dishonest member's pass, but still a pass. My god, it was all true! The place I'd been reaching for, searching, striving and grabbing at for years was upon me. Antwerp, that week, became the end of my shadily coloured Hoisters rainbow. Sitting down by the rain swept Dock front, Popeye boats a-bobbing, reminding me of Liverpools' all those years ago, I thought how I'd felt when the showroom manager introduced me to my brand new Saab a week before – my tenth or eleventh in the same number of years. Left alone, quietly at the controls, edging my way into the sumptuous leather seat, I started thinking: *is this it – the big deal?*

Brian, the immaculately dressed, Super Saab salesman, interrupting my thoughts good as Dennis the Eyebrows or any Florida Pier skater, asked. 'Is everything okay for you sir? Lovely model isn't it.'

'Err no…Err, I mean yeah. Give me a moment Brian.'

'Take your time sir. Just call if you need my assistance.'

I'd felt for the gear stick, running my hands over shiny upholstery. Are these the prizes you get for clawing and fighting your way out of rag-arse country? All those years of graft; all those pulled neck muscles from continually looking over your shoulder, and all that cagey headwork? It's only a car, metal and plastic, I mean, big deal! Sitting there, it washed into me and over me like drenching rain from a Dock Road walk that I felt exactly the same about the other stuff…New leather, Tetrad, three piece suite – big deal! Brand new, Hugo Boss suit – big deal! Expensive Bang and Olufsen stereo and new fitted kitchen – big fucken' deal! Didn't my New York guiding spirit, Johnny Lennon script the words, 'When your prize posses-sions start to weigh you down?' You could tell ol' Beatle balls had been through all that shit!

Thing is, I've found out the hard way, it really doesn't bring you any more ease with the world. And when you'd hear them forever rattling on about 'money can't buy you love, peace of mind, happiness etc', and how I used to think it was all a well-to-do conspiracy to keep the pauperized masses in their place, you know, to dampen down any dreamy notions the more boisterous among the poor might have about climbing over the mansion wall to grab a slice of velvet curtain for them-selves??? And when you'd hear people who owned charge cards for the finest stores, and fluffy white dogs who didn't shit on the sidewalk, continually saying, 'It's what's inside that counts; money or possessions never bring you any real joy', well, scuse me sir, but how was I to know how right the decently bank-balanced bastards were? It's the old cliché isn't it: 'Wish I'd known then what I know now'…

Thing is though, toddling along on two and a half of health, wealth and happiness, with Paddy and Boney then family, I didn't; and you were always less likely to listen to the voice of wisdom early days, while your belly was empty and your pants were falling down. Sound advice, if any, when early habits were being formed, was always bound to fall on deaf ears when you had no hope! Suppose some people were born to find out the hard way…

If you're the kid from a Town called Doledrum, you battle away, you leave school, you're up and running. Before you've had a chance to notice the difference between a pencil case and a toolbox, or what you're getting into, you're stuck on this Hamster wheel: give me some money, decent clobber, nice motor; cant climb off, mustn't slack; sleep, work, sleep again; weekend, work again. You're in the wheel. Next thing you find you've been chasing all over the show or, in my case, all over the World for twenty years; in search of what? Stuff! Or, some sort of holy pound note grail that leads to the Curtain Peep suburbs? I thought I knew. Since my *proper* mates bit the bullet and the underwater thing in Florida, its gone *seriously* fucked-up fuzzy!

There I was: health, wealth and half of happiness; bored, but coming to terms with what I was. Busy collecting material possessions and starting to click it was all just bric-a-brac, baggage and stuff. Nitty-gritty: a roof, warmth, bit of love, basic food and health, and enough money or lifting technique to pay for those things. It's all you need isn't it! And, face it; the Social fucken' Services give most of that shit to the first man off the boat these days! It's all free if you like sleeping in!

I got told by Thatcher and Tebbit I'd better get on my bike. But, just look at what they give you if you hardly venture from the council house armchair, never mind your own High Street: Vicky Pollard Baby machines – houses and money for dropping bastardized kids all over the inner city! Drug addicts – freshly painted flats and hand held detox! Pensioner puncher's – trips to the seaside, or trekking with a shrink in the Lake District! Food addicted, fat, lazy cunts – obesity videos, hospital beds and nurses who wipe your arse after every slurp! Brainwashed terrorists – legal aid and flats in North London! Its fucken' endless! Oh, and dare I say it, Shoplifters – re-education and psychology lessons that, to a man, none of them have got any interest in whatsoever, take it from a man in the know...

If you're a 'wrong-un' the politically correct fascists will make sure you're looked after. No wonder Pensioners elbow young people in bus stops. Britain ay, the new freebie handout zone, a career option and, I know, because I used them, and it, to remain hidden away for a few months till I noticed well-stacked shops with well-stacked prices.

So, welcome to the media driven techno age. A celebrity loving culture full of Posh Spice's, Bedraggled Brittany's and gormless fucken' Jade's plastered on posters, papers and TV. With Murdoch controlling most of what you see on TV, while brain dead Bush gives out his phony New Orleans hugs. Hmm...looks like money really has become the be-all and end-all. It seemed that way for me once...when I was skint at the foot of the mountain. And with Murdoch and Bush country people constantly bombarding us with money-mad advertisements for Armani, Versace, Burberry, Sony, BMW, Mercedes, and that consumerism and capitalism is good, and it all comes packaged in Louis Vuiton fucken' luggage, it's like there's nowhere left to escape or hide from it all...

Who knows, maybe find me and the family some freedom in New Zealand, or West Coast Australia? Thing is, I've tried; those fuckers won't let you in! Naively thought this Florida gaff might be the place, you know, to set me back on track after a piece of instant karma knocked me for six...Got to say, spiritually, I knew it was coming, just never sussed the moment...who does? Learning to read the inner and outer vibes before the big epiphany moment...pah!

Sadly for me, while looking for peace and quiet to work stuff out, the interruptions – like this prick-of-a-skater – come thick and fast. Since seeing that imminent white staircase for the second time, and the Karma thing, I'm going through the shoplifting motions; old habits refusing to die. I know I've got to though...

All's I need is a clear patch of breathing space to clear my head. Get a new act on the road. Some place with no phony, status symbol adverts jammed up in your face, and no loud-arse Porsche or Lexus engines revving themselves straight off the hording boards to blast a hole in your mindset! No corrupt suits and their rotten as fuck wheels of industry! No tactless, mid-evening, cold callers, interrupting dinner with timeshare, insurance or some other shit to sell! No jargon spouting, till-draw eye-lidded, corporate whores, offering finance deals to bind you for life! Some place under the stars to blend, chill and be left alone to put a few things to bed – for good!

Sometimes it feels like I'm one of these daft skaters, you know, on a set of wheels bound for nowhere. I badly want to be an ex-shoplifter and, maybe I'm getting there, but, till I do, suppose I'm just the same as any addict looking to avoid the real world with a bit of quick-hit-utopia. I know I've got to stop. I mean, I know it! Face it Mickey lad, it's time to exert all concentration and energy levels on putting an end to this Kleptomania thing.

Seeing as one of the skaters has left a bag behind, and they've all hit the road, think I need to get some sort of plan on the go. Wonder what's in the Walmart bag...? Coul be time for me to get me skates on...?

THE END